Brokenville
Philip Ridley

The Pilgrimage
Paul Goetzee

Philip Ridley was born in the East End of London, where he still lives and works. He studied painting at St Martin's School of Art and has exhibited throughout Europe, New York and Japan. As a writer he has written three adult novels and eight children's novels, including *Krindlekrax* (1991), winner of the Smarties Prize for Children's Fiction and the W. H. Smith Mind-Boggling Books Award, and a number of plays for radio. His plays for children include *Fairytaleheart* (Hampstead Theatre, 1998) and *Sparkleshark* (Royal National Theatre, 1999). His films include *The Krays* (1990) and *The Reflecting Skin* (1990).

Paul Goetzee lives in Liverpool. He has written for various national touring companies, and commissions include *Act of Faith* (Soho Theatre Company, 1994), *Venice* (Liverpool Playhouse, 1987) and *The Tinder Box* (Chester Gateway, 1988). He has written one short film for Channel Four (*The Return of Neville Dedd*, 1990) and written and directed an independent short film (*The Contender*, 2000). In between writing, he helps develop other writers' scripts with his company Productionline. He is married with three children.

CONNECTIONS

Brokenville
PHILIP RIDLEY

The Pilgrimage
PAUL GOETZEE

faber and faber

First published in this edition 2001
by Faber and Faber Limited
3 Queen Square London WC1N 3AU
Published in the United States by Faber and Faber, Inc.,
an affiliate of Farrar, Straus and Giroux, New York
The Pilgrimage was first published in *New Connections 99* in 1999

Typeset by Country Setting, Kingsdown, Kent CT14 8ES
Printed in England by Mackays of Chatham plc, Chatham, Kent

A CIP record for this book
is available from the British Library

ISBN 0-571-20609-3 (Faber edn)
ISBN 0-7487-4292-1 (Stanley Thornes edn)

2 4 6 8 10 9 7 5 3 1

Contents

Foreword from the Royal National Theatre vii

Brokenville 1

The Pilgrimage 81

Stanley Thornes online 119

Foreword

Most of the plays in this series were generated through a unique and epic project initiated by the Royal National Theatre, London, and funded by BT.

For many years the Education Department at the RNT had been receiving calls from youth theatre companies and schools asking us to recommend scripts for them to perform. They were looking for contemporary, sophisticated, unpatronising scripts with great plots and storylines, where the characters would fit the age range of the young people playing them. At that time, there weren't many plays written for the 11-to-19 age group. So we decided to approach the best writing talent around and ask them to write short plays specifically for young people.

In two-year cycles over a period of six years, we created a portfolio of new plays and invited 150 schools and youth theatres to choose the one that most excited them. We then invited the participants to come on a weekend retreat and work through the script with the writer before producing the play in their home venue. Some of those productions were then invited to one of ten festivals at professional theatres throughout the UK. Each two-year cycle culminated in a summer festival at the Royal National Theatre, where the stages, back-stage areas and foyers were ablaze with youthful energy and creativity.

But the story doesn't end there. As we've discovered, the UK isn't alone in demanding fantastic new scripts for the youth market. A fourth cycle is already under way, and this time the portfolio will include more contributions from overseas. As long as there's a need, we will continue to commission challenging work to feed the intelligence, imagination and ingenuity of young people and the adults with whom they work.

Suzy Graham-Adriani
Royal National Theatre
July 2000

For more information on the writers and the work involved on the BT/National Connections project, visit: www.nt-online.org

BROKENVILLE

Philip Ridley

Stories are for joining the past to the future.
Stories are for those late hours in the night
when you can't remember how you got from
where you were to where you are. Stories are
for eternity, when memory is erased, when there is
nothing to remember except the story.

Tim O'Brian

Characters

Child

Satchel

Glitter

Quiff

Bruise

Tattoo

Old Woman

Night.
   Twinkling stars.
   Ethereal moonlight reveals –

A ruined house: no ceiling, near-demolished walls,
smashed windows, stairway. Several piles of rubble.
A big puddle.

Signs of family life are scattered everywhere; framed
photographs, toys, etc. Also, a bed, table, chairs.
Everything damaged by some nameless catastrophe. In
the moonlight this becomes a dreamscape of broken
memory.

Child is in the building. He is ten years old. His clothes –
T-shirt, jeans and trainers – all bear signs of whatever
has gone before. He is holding a small music box.

Child gets into bed, tucks blanket around him, and
opens the music box.
   A gentle, haunting lullaby starts to play.

Child opens book of fairy tales. The pages are little more
than tatters, but he stares as if reading, finding comfort
in this instinctive ritual. Child sinks lower into bed and
pulls blanket up around him.
   Gradually, he drifts into sleep . . .

Pause

A sixteen-year-old male enters, clutching satchel and
torch. He is wearing a dishevelled school uniform. He

7

has an intense, studious manner, enhanced by his short hair and glasses. He will be referred to as Satchel.

Satchel searches the ruined house with his torch.
  The light comes to rest on Child.

Slowly, Satchel approaches Child.
  Child is gently moaning in his sleep.
  The music box continues playing . . .

Satchel goes to puddle. He stares into water for a while, then sits nearby. He continues gazing into water.

Pause.

A fourteen-year-old female enters, clutching torch. She is wearing a dress (decorated with silver sequins) and silver stilettos. Her face is fully made-up (albeit smudged) and there is glitter in her hair. She will be referred to as Glitter.

Glitter Anyone here?
Satchel Me. Who're you?
Glitter I'm . . . don't remember.

  Approaches Satchel.

What's your name?
Satchel Forgotten.

  Slight pause.

Glitter I . . . I've got glitter in my hair.
Satchel I'm holding a satchel.
Glitter What's in it?
Satchel Pens. A notebook.
Glitter It might have your name in.
Satchel Just blank pages.

  Glitter aims torch at Child.

Glitter I heard the . . . what's it called?

Hums to music.

Satchel Music.
Glitter Music! Yes!
Satchel Heard it too.
Glitter Nothing to do with you, then?
Satchel What?
Glitter The child.
Satchel No.

Slight pause.

Were you at a party?
Glitter Party?
Satchel Your dress. Hair.
Glitter Oh . . . suppose I must've been.

Slight pause.

What happened?
Satchel Where?
Glitter Everywhere.
Satchel Don't remember.
Glitter No. I don't. Nothing.

Indicates Satchel's wristwatch.

What's the time?
Satchel It's stopped. Midnight.

*A fourteen-year-old male enters, clutching torch. He is
well built and wearing jeans, leather jacket and white
T-shirt. His hair is styled in a quiff. He has a brash,
cocksure manner, and will be referred to as Quiff.*

Satchel (*with Glitter*) Who's there?
Glitter (*with Satchel*) Who's there?
Quiff Who're you first?

Approaches Satchel and Glitter.

9

Satchel I've got a satchel.
Glitter I've got glitter in my hair.

Quiff goes to puddle, looks at reflection and combs hair.

Satchel You hear the music too?
Quiff What if I did?
Glitter Can you remember your name?
Quiff 'Course I can.
Satchel What is it, then?
Quiff . . . Not telling.
Glitter He's forgotten.
Satchel We've all forgotten.
Quiff Everyone liked my quiff. Remember that. Everyone wanted to . . . to . . .

Slight pause.

Stuff with lips.
Satchel Kiss you?
Quiff Snog me.
Glitter I don't.
Quiff (*indicating Satchel*) He does.
Satchel Don't!
Quiff Liar!

Child starts murmuring in his sleep again.
  Quiff aims torch at Child, then goes to him.

Quiff Anything to do with you two?
Glitter What?
Quiff The kid.
Glitter (*with Satchel*) No. Not ours.
Satchel (*with Glitter*) No, no.

Quiff takes blanket from Child and wraps it round his shoulders.

Glitter (*at Satchel*) Should we stop him?

Quiff sits in corner and continues combing his hair.

Satchel You got a watch?
Quiff Eh?
Glitter The time.

Quiff looks at his wristwatch.

Quiff Midnight.
Satchel It's not.
Quiff Can tell the bloody time.
Satchel You'll find it's stopped.

Quiff puts wristwatch to ear.

Satchel Am I right?
Quiff Leave me alone.

A fifteen-year-old female enters, clutching a torch. She is wearing dark dress, dark cardigan, an engagement ring, and a single earring. There's a bruise on her left leg. There's a becalmed melancholy about her. She'll be referred to as Bruise.

Satchel (*with Glitter*) Who's there?
Glitter (*with Satchel*) Who's there?
Bruise Just me, just me.

Slight pause.

Who're you?
Satchel Got a satchel.
Glitter Got glitter.

Slight pause.

Satchel He's got a quiff.
Bruise Well . . . I've got a bruise.
Glitter How that happen?
Bruise . . . Forgotten.

Aims torch at Child.

11

That . . . music. I heard it from . . . wherever I was.
It's so . . .
Glitter Beautiful?
Bruise No. I mean, yes. It is. But that's not the word . . .

Slight pause.

A thing for children.
Glitter Nursery rhyme?
Bruise To help them sleep.
Satchel Lullaby.
Bruise Lullaby! Yes!

*A fifteen-year-old male enters. He is stocky, with a
closely shaven head, and wearing army-surplus style
trousers and shirt. A tattoo is visible on his arm.
There's a bandage stuck over his left eye. He'll be
referred to as Tattoo.*

Satchel (*with others*) Who's there?
Glitter (*with others*) Who's there?
Bruise (*with others*) Who's that?
Tattoo I'll ask the questions. Who're you?
Satchel Satchel.
Glitter Glitter.
Tattoo (*at Bruise*) You?
Bruise . . . What?
Tattoo Name!
Glitter She's got a bruise.
Bruise Yes. I'm Bruise.
Tattoo (*at Quiff*) You?
Satchel Quiff.
Tattoo Ain't he got a tongue?
Glitter Just for snogging.

Slight pause.

What've you got?
Tattoo Eh?

Satchel For your name.
Tattoo Name? My name's . . .

Slight pause.

Got a tattoo.
Satchel Show me.

Looks at tattoo.

What is it?
Tattoo Some . . . thing.
Bruise What's it mean?
Tattoo Forgotten.

Winces at pain in eye.

Glitter What happened?
Tattoo Not sure.
Satchel He's forgotten.
Glitter Everything's forgotten.
Bruise Should bathe it. Your eye.
Satchel Use the puddle.

Tattoo goes to puddle and bathes eye.

Satchel You got the time?
Tattoo Watch stopped.
Satchel (*with Glitter*) Midnight.
Glitter (*with Satchel*) Midnight.

Old Woman enters, clutching torch. She is in her eighties, wearing many layers of frayed jumpers, and walks with the aid of a stick. Like the others, her clothes bear signs of whatever has gone before.

Satchel (*with others*) Who's there?
Glitter (*with others*) Who's there?
Bruise (*with others*) Who's that?
Tattoo (*with others*) Identify yourself.

Old Woman Don't get your knickers in a twist. An old woman. That's all.

Aims torch at them.

Who're you lot?
Satchel Satchel.
Glitter Glitter.
Bruise Bruise.
Tattoo Tattoo.
Old Woman (*at Quiff*) Lost your tongue?
Satchel He's Quiff.
Old Woman (*indicating Child*) What about this one?
Bruise He's not ours.
Old Woman One of the lost, eh?

The music box has been winding down.
    Now it stops.
    Child wakes in panic and jumps from bed.

Old Woman Don't be scared. (*At others.*) Stop shining your torches at him.

Approaches Child.

It's all right.

Child backs away.

Old Woman I'm not going to hurt you.

Moves closer to Child.

You're safe now.

Gradually, Old Woman makes her way to Child.
    She wraps her arms around him.

Old Woman He's petrified. And cold. Make a fire someone.

Pause.

14

Can't you help a child? Forgotten how to do that? – Oi!
Tattoo! Fire!
Tattoo All right, all right.

Starts looking for firewood.

Old Woman (*at Bruise*) Wakey-wakey! A fire needs
things to burn. Remember?
Bruise Oh . . . yes. Sorry.

Starts looking.

Old Woman Don't burn anything that hasn't been
damaged. Just broken stuff. This is still someone's home.
Hear me?
Bruise Of course, yes.
Tattoo All right, all right.

*Tattoo and Bruise start making pile of objects in
middle of room.*

Satchel You know the time?
Old Woman No.
Bruise You know what happened?
Old Woman No.
Glitter You know where we are?
Old Woman No, no, no. Why all the questions? The
time? Sometime! What happened? Something! The place?
At the moment it's a cold place – Coldville! Ha! How's
that? – Where's the bloody fire?
Tattoo Nearly there.

Child is watching Tattoo and Bruise search.
    Old Woman keeps her eye on Child.
    Slight pause.

Bruise finds dead bird.
    Child points at it.

Old Woman What?

15

Child still points.

Old Woman What you got there?
Bruise A bird.
Satchel Cockatoo.
Old Woman Someone's pet probably.

Child reaches out for dead bird.

Slight pause.

Old Woman Give it to him.

Bruise gives Child the dead bird.

Old Woman Light the fire! Come on. Chop-chop.
Tattoo Got any matches?
Old Woman Why? You got a cigarette? Ha!

Slight pause.

Tattoo (*at Quiff*) What about you?
Quiff What?
Tattoo Matches? Lighter?
Quiff What if I have?
Tattoo Quickly!

Quiff gives lighter to Tattoo.
  Tattoo sets fire to pile of objects.
  Child starts whimpering at firelight.

Old Woman Only a little fire. Don't worry.
Tattoo What's he afraid of?

Child continues to whimper.
  Old Woman notices storybook.

Old Woman What's this . . .? Fairy stories? You like fairy stories?

Child calms a little.

Old Woman Want me to tell you one?

16

Slight pause.

Do you?

Child nods.

Old Woman A story it shall be!

Opens book and reads.

'There was a land called . . .'

Peers closer.

Oh . . . the pages are torn.

Child begins whimpering again.

Old Woman Don't panic. I'll think of something.

Slight pause.

There was once a land where everything . . . was in
ruins. Like this place. No one knew what had caused
everything to be broken. But broken it was. And this
land was called . . .
Satchel Brokenville?
Old Woman What –? Oh, yes! Very good. Brokenville.
Now we're getting somewhere. There was once a
land called Brokenville. And, like all fairy-tale lands,
it had a . . .
Satchel Castle!
Old Woman Exactly! (*at Child*) You see the top of that
wall? The jagged brick. That's just what the turret looked
like . . . Now what?

*Child plucks feather from dead bird and gives it to
Old Woman.*

Old Woman A feather?
Satchel He wants a story about a feather.

Child nods.

Old Woman Well, if that's what you want, that's what you'll get. Let's see . . .

Slight pause.

In Brokenville Castle there lived a King.
Satchel And Queen?
Old Woman Of course. The King and Queen of Brokenville. And the Queen . . . oh, she loved the King very much.
Satchel And the King loved her.
Old Woman No. The King couldn't stand the sight of her. In fact, she made him puke.
Satchel Why?
Old Woman Battles and wars! That's all the King's life had been. Wars and battles. And so now his heart . . . well, he had no heart.
Satchel Just a big nothing.
Old Woman No love.
Bruise Poor Queen.
Old Woman Oh, she was very upset.
Satchel What did she do?

Slight pause.

What did the Queen – ?
Old Woman Give me a chance, cleverclogs.

Slight pause.

A Wizard! That's it! The Queen went to see a Wizard. And she said, 'I love the King more than life itself, but the King . . . well, I make him puke. Tell me, Wizard, what can I do to make the King love me?'
Satchel What does he say?
Old Woman You tell me . . . Wizard Satchel.
Satchel Me? But . . . oh, I forget how to –
Old Woman Forget! said the Wizard. Forget all about the King. Very good, Wizard Satchel. But the Queen

said, 'I can't forget the King. Not just like that. You'll have to think of something better. Hear me? You'll have to try harder, Wizard Satchel.'

Slight pause.

What about a magic song?
Satchel Good idea! I'll teach you a magic song.
Old Woman And have I got to sing it to the King? asked the Queen.
Satchel That's right. Every night. As he sleeps.
Old Woman Then what? asked the Queen.

Slight pause.

Chop-chop.
Satchel If, after singing this song . . . thirty-six times, you still make the King puke then . . . well, you won't be bothered.
Bruise Why?
Satchel Because . . .
Old Woman Because after singing the song thirty-six times, said Wizard Satchel, if the King doesn't love you, then you will stop loving him. Right?
Satchel Right.
Old Woman What d'you think of that? (*at Bruise*) Queen Bruise?
Bruise . . . Me? Why me?
Old Woman It's about singing to a husband.
Bruise So?
Old Woman You're wearing an engagement ring.
Bruise Oh . . . yes.
Glitter Is it real gold?
Tattoo Why you getting married?
Satchel Did you have to?
Quiff Where's your bloke now?
Bruise I don't remember. Nothing. Why? Why?
Old Woman Don't worry about remembering. Just sing.

Bruise But . . . is that possible? You know? To sing a song and stop loving? Just like that?
Old Woman It's magic. Anything's possible. Sing!

Slight pause.

Bruise . . . Nothing.
Old Woman Something will come. Some fragment. Trust me.

Pause.
 Then –

Bruise
 Rock . . . a-bye, baby . . .
 On the treetop.
 When the wind . . . blows
 The cradle will rock.
 When the bough breaks
 The cradle will fall.
 Down will come baby,
 Cradle and all.

 Slight pause.

Old Woman For thirty-six nights the Queen sang this song. And for thirty-six mornings she asked the King . . .
Bruise . . . Love me?
Old Woman And for thirty-six mornings the King replied . . .

 Old Woman looks at Tattoo.
  Child looks at Tattoo.
  Others look at Tattoo.

Tattoo . . . Me?
Old Woman Oh, do wake up. (*at Child*) The King was notoriously thick in the mornings. (*at Tattoo*) Do you love this girl?
Tattoo No.

Old Woman Said King Tattoo.

Slight pause.

And then, on the night the Queen sang her magic song
for the thirty-sixth time, she felt something shift inside her.
Bruise Shift?
Old Woman Kick.
Bruise I'm . . . pregnant.
Tattoo Pregnant!
Old Woman Gasped King Tattoo.
Bruise Want to hold me now?
Tattoo No.
Bruise Don't you feel anything?
Tattoo You make me puke.
Bruise Good.
Tattoo What's going on?
Bruise When . . . when my baby's born – oh, yes! That'll
love me. Hear me? I know I'm too young. But I'm going
to make a great mother. I'll look after it really well.
Don't care what anyone thinks! Don't care what *you*
think!
Tattoo Well, I don't give a toss what you –

Winces at sudden pain in eye.

Old Woman The next day King Tattoo felt a pain in his
eye.
Satchel Pain got worse and worse.
Old Woman It started to bleed.
Satchel Big clots of black blood.
Old Woman Then a frog jumped out.
Tattoo A frog?
Old Woman King Tattoo was surprised.
Tattoo King Tattoo thinks it's stupid.
Old Woman Next day he had a lump on his arm.

Slight pause.

What d'you do?

Tattoo Eh?

Old Woman That lump on your arm. Like a boil. We want to know what you're going to do about it. (*at Child*) Don't we?

Child nods.

Tattoo Lance it.

Satchel He cuts it open.

Old Woman What jumps out?

Tattoo . . . A frog?

Old Woman Very good. And now you've got to find out what's wrong with you. (*at Child*) Hasn't he?

Child nods.

Tattoo But . . . how?

Old Woman Ask the Wizard, stupid. Go on.

Slight pause.

Chop-chop!

Tattoo What's wrong with me?

Satchel What're the symptoms?

Tattoo Frog growing.

Satchel You're suffering from . . . Frog Growing Disease.

Tattoo Mmm, I see.

Old Woman Ask what it means, King Tattoo. Go on.

Tattoo What does Frog Growing Disease mean?

Satchel You're dying.

Tattoo I'm not.

Old Woman Ask him why, King Tattoo?

Tattoo . . . Why?

Satchel Because . . . no one loves you.

Tattoo They do!

Satchel Who?

Tattoo Her! Queen Bruise.

Bruise You make me puke.

Tattoo Other people then.
Satchel Who? Give me phone numbers.

Slight pause.

Tattoo I . . . can't remember.
Satchel Then you're dying.
Old Woman Say it!

Slight pause.

Tattoo I'm dying.
Old Woman There's an alternative, you know.
Tattoo What?
Old Woman (*at Satchel*) Tell him, Wizard Satchel.

Slight pause.

Satchel If . . . if you manage to find something that loves
you, then the frogs will stop growing. You'll live.
Tattoo And . . . if I don't find something?
Old Woman Your heart will stop beating when your
child is born.

Pause.

Bruise Search, then!
Tattoo I am.
Old Woman You don't find love sitting on your bum.

*Tattoo takes a few steps round the building.
    As he reaches the puddle –*

Old Woman One day, as the King walked along the
bank of a river, he heard a cry for help. He looked and
saw a . . . fish.
Tattoo A fish?
Old Woman Trapped in some weeds.
Tattoo So . . . what happens?
Old Woman You tell us.
Tattoo I cook it.

Bruise You're looking for love, not dinner.
Tattoo Rescue it!
Old Woman Then you say . . .
Tattoo I . . . rescued you, Little Fish. So now I want you to . . . to . . .
Bruise He can't say it.
Tattoo Can!
Satchel Can't!
Tattoo Can! Can!
Old Woman Prove it!
Tattoo Love me!

Slight pause.

Old Woman But Little Fish replied . . .

Looks at Child.

Yes, you. What did the fish reply?

Child whispers in Old Woman's ear.

Old Woman Little Fish says, No.
Tattoo Why?
Old Woman Because you don't want love. Not *real* love. You just want gratitude. (*at Child*) Right?

Child nods.

Bruise Clever fish.
Old Woman And Little Fish swam away from the King as fast as he could. Splash, splash.

Child makes splashing noises.

Old Woman Oh, very good.

Slight pause.

The next day the King found . . . (*at Child*) What?

Child points at sky.

Old Woman A star?

Child points to the ground.

Old Woman A fallen star!

Child nods.

Bruise What d'you do, King Tattoo?
Tattoo Rescue it.
Old Woman Throw it back to the sky.

Tattoo throws star up.

Bruise He'll ask you to love him now.
Tattoo Love me, Fallen Star.
Old Woman But Fallen Star said . . .

Child whispers in Old Woman's ear.

Old Woman Ha! Very good. Twinkle, twinkle. Which
roughly translates as: Why should I love a meat-head
like you?
Tattoo What you call me?
Old Woman Answer the question!
Tattoo No!
Old Woman (*with Bruise*) Answer!
Bruise (*with Old Woman*) Answer!

Slight pause.

Tattoo Because . . . I'm very strong. No one else could . . .
throw you back like I did. That's why you should love me.
How's that?

Child whispers in Old Woman's ear.

Tattoo What's he say?
Old Woman Twinkle, twinkle.
Tattoo What's that mean?
Old Woman You don't want love. You want admiration.
And Fallen Star turned its twinkling away from the King.

Child looks away from Tattoo.

Bruise Clever star.
Tattoo You've all made your minds up about me. It's not fair! I'm not playing any more.
Old Woman The King was on the brink of giving up when he found an egg.

Slight pause.

Find it!
Bruise Go on!
Old Woman (*with Satchel*) Go on!
Satchel (*with Old Woman*) Go on!
Tattoo Stop bloody ordering me around!

Child is distressed by sudden outburst.

Old Woman You're upsetting the child.
Bruise (*with Satchel*) Find it!
Satchel (*with Bruise*) Find it!
Old Woman Chop-chop!

Child's distress is increasing.

Tattoo All right, all right.

Starts looking.

There is no egg!
Old Woman Anything young will do.
Tattoo . . . Young?

Old Woman indicates Child.

Slight pause.

Tattoo approaches Child.
    Child whimpers in panic.

Old Woman Shush! It's all right. He won't hurt you. (*At Tattoo.*) Will you?

Tattoo 'Course not.

Slight pause.

Hello, Little Egg.
Old Woman (*at Child*) You see? He's not as scary as he
looks.

Child calms.

Tattoo What now?
Old Woman You tell us.

Slight pause.

Tattoo I'll . . . I'll take this Little Egg . . . somewhere
secret.
Old Woman The forest?
Tattoo Yes.
Old Woman And look after it?
Tattoo Yes.
Old Woman And when it hatches?
Tattoo I'll make it love me.
Old Woman So that's what the King did. He stayed in
the forest and looked after Little Egg. Until, one day, he
heard a hatching sound . . . (*at Child*) Hatching sound, if
you please.

Child makes a hatching noise.

Old Woman And he saw?
Tattoo An eye!

Child makes hatching noise.

Old Woman What now?
Tattoo A beak!

Child makes hatching noise.

Tattoo A baby bird!

Child opens mouth.

Tattoo What's it doing?
Old Woman It's hungry.
Bruise Feed it.
Tattoo With what?
Old Woman Chewed worms.

Slight pause.

Go on.

Tattoo chews.
  He goes to hand imaginary worms to Child.

Old Woman Not like that.
Glitter Like a bird.
Bruise Beak to beak.

Slight pause.

Old Woman Chop-chop.

Tattoo leans toward Child.
  Closer . . .
  Closer . . .

Bruise Baby Bird is fed!
Old Woman And, after thirty-six days of caring for his Baby Bird, the King asked . . .

Slight pause.

Tattoo . . . Love me?
Old Woman Baby Bird replied . . .

Child whispers in Old Woman's ear.

Old Woman Yes.
Bruise You sure?
Old Woman He's sure.
Tattoo Back to the Castle!

Old Woman King Tattoo put Baby Bird in a cage. And he kept it secretly in his room.
Glitter Why?
Old Woman So it can never love anyone else. Right?
Tattoo Good idea.

Bruise tuts irritably.

Old Woman Queen Bruise – oh, she was becoming irritated.
Bruise What's in your room?
Tattoo Something that loves me.
Bruise You! Loved! Ha!
Old Woman One day the Queen's child was born.
Bruise What –? Oh, yes! My baby.
Glitter Boy or girl?
Bruise Boy. Hoped it would be a boy. Already painted the nursery blue. Look at his little hands.
Old Woman Look, King Tattoo.
Bruise His fingers. See?
Tattoo Mmm.
Bruise So perfect. And look! Here! A birthmark on his leg. See?
Tattoo Yeah.
Bruise Your son.
Tattoo My . . . son.
Bruise We'll look after it together.

Slight pause.

Old Woman King Tattoo went to Wizard Satchel.
Tattoo I do?
Old Woman Baby born? You alive?
Tattoo Oh, right! Yeah! – Hey, Wizard Satchel. I'm still alive. And look! No frogs. That means I'm not going to cop it. Right?
Satchel We all cop it eventually.
Tattoo You know what I bloody mean.

Satchel You won't cop it.

Slight pause.

Old Woman So . . . the King went back to Baby Bird's cage and opened the door.
Tattoo Clear off! Don't need you any more. Migrate or something.
Old Woman Baby Bird flew out of its cage.

Child flaps his arms.

Old Woman Oh, very good.
Tattoo Goodbye, Baby Bird.

Slight pause.

Satchel And . . . that's the end of the story?
Old Woman Not sure? (*at Child*) Is it?

Child shakes his head.

Old Woman 'Course not! I know! Being in the cage for so long must have driven Baby Bird mad. Right?

Child nods.

Old Woman Baby Bird flew round the Castle in a frenzy.
Satchel Catch it!
Bruise Catch it!
Glitter There it goes!
Tattoo What's going on?
Old Woman And then . . . one feather . . .

Holds up feather.

Goes into the open mouth of the baby Prince.
Bruise You can't.
Old Woman Can! One feather goes into the baby's mouth. No one noticed. By the time Baby Bird had been driven from the Castle, the feather had –
Bruise Don't! Please!

Old Woman The feather had choked the Queen's child.

Slight pause.

Happy with that?

Child nods.
   Child takes feather from Old Woman.
   Child puts it on the fire.
   Pause.

Old Woman We should look for more things to burn?
(*at Child*) What d'you think?

Child nods.

Old Woman Don't want to put the fire out, do we? –
Oi! Satchel!
Satchel Yes, yes, all right. (*at Child*) Wanna help?
Old Woman (*at Child*) Well?

Child nods.

Old Woman Go on, then.

Child looks for things.

Old Woman Oi! Quiff! Make yourself useful.

Quiff doesn't move.

Satchel Hello, what's this?

Picks something up.

Oh . . . no, never mind.

Child tries to see.

Old Woman Show him!
Satchel It's a tooth.
Old Woman What kind?
Satchel . . . Human.

Old Woman Say so, then. You've found a human tooth.
Say it.
Satchel . . . I've found a human tooth.

Child leads Satchel to fire.

Satchel Wh . . . what's he want?
Old Woman The story of the tooth. (*At Child.*) Right?

Child nods.

Old Woman Gather round, everyone. Chop-chop.

Child and Satchel sit by fire.
Others cluster round.
Pause.

Satchel There was once a land called Brokenville.
Old Woman Very good. Go on.
Satchel And . . . in this land there was . . .
Bruise Queen Bruise?
Satchel Yes.

Child shakes his head.
He whispers in Old Woman's ear.

Bruise What's wrong?
Old Woman No Queen.

Slight pause.

Satchel In Brokenville there was a King –

Child shakes his head.
He whispers in Old Woman's ear.

Old Woman No King.
Satchel Where are they, then?

Child whispers in Old Woman's ear.

Old Woman Oh, that's wonderful. (*At others.*) The
Queen collects seashells. But . . . well, the nearest beach

in Brokenville – oh, it's miles and miles from the Castle.
And very difficult to get to. In fact, it's the most difficult
place to get to in the whole of Brokenville.
Satchel And the most beautiful, I bet.
Glitter So the King's taken her there.
Bruise He does it once a year.
Old Woman And while they're gone . . . guess who they
leave in charge?

Child whispers in Old Woman's ear.

Old Woman Their son.
Quiff Prince Quiff!

Child claps excitedly.
Quiff moves toward the fire.

Old Woman What a dishy Prince.
Glitter He's vain enough already.
Satchel Prince Quiff is a vain prince.
Quiff With reason. Look at my hair. My eyelashes. And
look –

Lifts T-shirt.

What a six-pack. I am perfection.
Satchel The Prince would look in the mirror and say . . .

Quiff goes to puddle.

Quiff Wotcha, gorgeous.

Slight pause.

Wanna touch me quiff, Satch?

Slight pause.

Go on. You know you want to.

Slowly, Satchel reaches out to touch the quiff.
Just as his finger is about to make contact –

33

Quiff Well, you can't. Ha!

Glitter Oh, that's nasty.

Bruise Bully.

Satchel (*at Quiff*) You think I'm just a joke, don't you!

Quiff Gonna cry, Satch?

Satchel . . . No.

Quiff Liar!

Satchel Stop calling me that!

Quiff What you gonna do about it?

Satchel turns away.

Old Woman (*at Satchel*) Get your own back.

Glitter Yeah. Say something.

Bruise Do something.

Satchel What's the point? People like . . . like him – they always win.

Old Woman Not when you're telling the story.

Slowly, Satchel turns to face them all.
Slight pause.

Satchel The Prince . . . he spent all his time gazing into mirrors. Saying, 'Kiss me! Kiss me! Kiss me!'

Quiff You've gotta be joking.

Old Woman Go on.

Quiff No way.

Child starts whimpering.

Old Woman Look what you're doing! The story. Do it!

Bruise (*with Glitter*) Chop-chop!

Glitter (*with Bruise*) Chop-chop!

Quiff Kiss me! Kiss me! Kiss me!

Child calms.

Satchel And then, one day, the Prince kissed a mirror so hard it cracked. He cut his lip.

Child whimpers again.

Old Woman It wasn't a big cut, I'm sure.
Satchel Tiny.
Old Woman And what happened?

Slight pause.

Did something crawl inside?
Satchel Yeah. That's it.
Tattoo Something very small.
Old Woman Well, I'd guessed that much.
Satchel An insect.
Old Woman Very good. And?

Slight pause.

Did it do something to the Prince?
Satchel It . . . went into his bloodstream.
Old Woman And?
Satchel It . . . made the Prince very ill.
Quiff Careful, Satchel.
Satchel His hair started to fall out.
Quiff I'm warning you –
Satchel Threatened Prince Quiff.
Old Woman But it did no good.
Glitter More hair fell out.
Bruise Handfuls.
Satchel Until he was bald.
Quiff No!
Satchel Yes!
Glitter (*with Bruise*) Well done, Satchel.
Bruise (*with Glitter*) Yes! Well done.
Quiff I'm not playing any more!

Storms to corner.

Old Woman If you don't like the story, change it.
Quiff Don't want to.

Glitter Can't do it!
Quiff Can!
Old Woman Prove it!

Slight pause.

Quiff returns from corner.

Quiff The King and Queen – they've gone to . . . to . . .
Satchel Brokenville Beach.
Quiff And I'm in charge, right?
Old Woman The Kingdom is yours.
Quiff And the people?
Old Woman We're your humble subjects.
Quiff Shave your heads!
Glitter He can't do that.
Old Woman I think he can.
Quiff Get shaving.
Satchel So . . . the humble subjects shaved their heads.
Quiff Ha! Clever or what? I'm the most perfect thing in the land again. Oh – what's this?

Looks at his reflection in puddle.

Wotcha, gorgeous.
Satchel And then Prince Quiff got thinner.
Quiff Thinner?
Satchel He locked himself in his room and cried for . . . oh, let's see, twenty-eight days and twenty-eight nights.
Old Woman Go to your room.
Bruise (*with Glitter*) Chop-chop.
Glitter (*with Bruise*) Chop-chop.

Quiff goes to corner.

Quiff How thin do I get?
Satchel All your muscles wither away.
Quiff What about me six-pack?
Old Woman Gone.

Satchel Without his looks, he's nothing.
Old Woman (*at Child*) Wonder what he's going to do, eh? Prince Quiff was very clever before, wasn't he? Wonder if her can do it again.

Quiff returns from corner.

Quiff Stop eating!
Bruise What?
Quiff Get as thin as me.
Glitter That's going too far.
Old Woman That's the law.
Satchel Everyone stopped eating until they were as thin as the Prince.

Quiff looks at his reflection.

Quiff Wotcha, gorgeous.
Satchel And then he spat out a tooth.

Holds up tooth.

Glitter His teeth are falling out.
Satchel The Prince locked himself –
Quiff I'm going.

Goes to corner.

Glitter Wait for it . . .

Slight pause.

Quiff returns from the corner.

Quiff Pull your teeth out.
Glitter Knew it!
Satchel And the Prince travelled the land looking at the piles of teeth and hair.
Quiff Kiss me! Kiss me! Kiss me!
Satchel Now cough blood.
Quiff B–blood?

Satchel Lots.
Glitter He's dying.
Quiff No.
Old Woman Yes.
Quiff Satch?
Old Woman Go to your room.
Quiff It's *his* story.

Points at Satchel.

Old Woman Go! Go!

Quiff goes to corner.

Bruise What's he gonna do?
Old Woman Don't know. (*At Child.*) Do we?

Quiff returns from corner.

Quiff Kill yourselves.
Satchel What?
Quiff Living is illegal if I'm not alive.

Child shakes his head and whispers in Old Woman's ear.

Old Woman He says you can't do that.
Quiff But I'm using the story. Like you said.
Old Woman You're using it in the wrong way.
Glitter You're being nasty.
Bruise Too cruel!
Tattoo You won't get away with it.
Old Woman Rebellion in Brokenville!
Tattoo Punish him!
Quiff What you gonna do?
Old Woman (*at Child*) What d'you think?

Child whispers in Old Woman's ear.

Old Woman Attack the Castle!
Tattoo Arm yourselves.

Child whispers in Old Woman's ear.

Old Woman Get the Prince!
Glitter Then what?

Child whispers in Old Woman's ear.

Old Woman Tear him to pieces!
Quiff No!
Tattoo Yes!

Quiff backs away from them.

Old Woman Don't let him escape!
Tattoo Catch him! Catch him!
Satchel (*with Tattoo*) Don't let him escape! Catch him!
(*etc.*)
Glitter (*with Tattoo*) Let me get my hands on him!
Catch him! (*etc.*)
Bruise (*with Tattoo*) He's a bad Prince! Catch him! (*etc.*)

Tattoo, Satchel, Glitter and Bruise are closing in on Quiff.

Quiff Don't hurt me! Please!
Tattoo Kill him!
All (*except Quiff and Child*) Kill! Kill! Kill! Kill!
Quiff (*screaming*) Nooooooooooooooooo!

Silence.
  Pause.
  Then –

Old Woman The Prince is dead.

Child – who's been enjoying the whole thing – now claps ecstatically.

Old Woman (*at Child*) You enjoyed that, didn't you?

Child nods, then whispers in Old Woman's ear.

Old Woman Feed the Prince to the birds.

Child makes squawking noises.
  Slight pause.
  Then –

Hauntingly, they all make squawking noises.
  They flash their torchlight everywhere.
  Slowly, the squawks fade away . . .
  Pause.

Glitter Perhaps the Prince's blood is magic.
Old Woman Magic?
Glitter Perhaps it made . . . well, everyone's hair grow back.
Bruise And their teeth.
Satchel Made them not thin any more.
Glitter Yes. Oh, yes.
Old Woman (*at Child*) What d'ya think?

Child shakes his head.

Glitter But why?
Old Woman He's right.
Satchel Everyone's alive.
Old Woman That's enough.
Quiff No magic blood.

Slight pause.

Old Woman Where's the tooth?
Satchel Here.

Child takes tooth from Satchel and puts it on the fire.
  Slight pause.
  Then –

Child points.

Old Woman What?

Child still points.

Bruise Something over here.

Goes to some shelves.

The vase?

Child shakes his head.

Bruise This?

Holds up broken piece of mirror.
Child nods.

Glitter What is it?
Bruise A piece of mirror.

Child sits in front of fire.

Old Woman (*at Bruise*) You know what to do.

Bruise goes to fire.
Others gather around her.
Slight pause.

Bruise There was once a . . .
Glitter Princess Glitter?
Bruise No.
Tattoo King Tattoo?
Bruise Yes.

Slight pause.

But he was a blind King.
Tattoo Why?
Bruise Because you once had a Queen. And you didn't show her enough love. The Queen died of a broken heart. And, once she was dead, you realised just how much you really cared for her. You cried your eyes out.

Child claps excitedly.

41

Bruise Every day the King walked in the garden of the Castle.

Old Woman The garden belonged to your dead Queen.

Bruise And the smell of her flowers – yes! It brings you comfort.

Tattoo But I can't see it, right?

Glitter Your son describes it to you.

Slight pause.

Old Woman Prince Quiff?

Quiff I thought the Prince was dead.

Old Woman New story, new Prince.

Tattoo puts hand on Quiff's shoulder.
Child claps with delight.

Tattoo Describe the garden, Prince Quiff.

Quiff Oh . . . it's not bad. Yellow climbing flowers – Oh, what they called?

Tattoo Roses?

Quiff That's it! Roses! All over the walls. And they're all around the border too. And the blue rose tree in each corner. There. How's that?

Old Woman Very good.

Glitter Yes. Good.

Bruise There was nothing King Tattoo liked to do more than sit in the dead Queen's garden and . . . smell the roses.

Tattoo sniffs.

Tattoo . . . Very flowery.

Slight pause.

Bruise And then, one day, a Dragon flew out of the sky.

Old Woman (*at Child*) They're scary, those Dragons.

Satchel Where did it come from?

Old Woman From . . . from the nearby mountains.

Child whispers in Old Woman's ear.

Old Woman Good point. (*At Bruise.*) Why hadn't anyone seen the Dragon before?

Bruise Because . . . because the Dragon hadn't smelt the roses. That's it. You see, the roses had been growing and growing. More and more every year. And now . . . well, the Castle was full of them. And . . . there's nothing Dragons like more than to eat roses. But, King Tattoo didn't want the Dragon to eat his garden so . . .

Tattoo I'll see Wizard Satchel. (*At Child.*) Right?

Child nods approvingly.
Tattoo goes to Satchel.

Tattoo That Dragon's going to munch my garden. Do something.

Satchel The Dragon's not greedy. Take my advice. Give it a corner of your garden. Grow roses just for the Dragon. I'm sure it'll be happy and leave the rest of your garden alone.

Tattoo I'm not having that overgrown lizard stomping around like he owns the place. Where's my son? Prince!

Slight pause.

Prince Quiff!

Quiff Oh . . . sorry! Here! Wotcha, King Tatt.

Tattoo Kill the Dragon. And don't call me Tatt.

Quiff But Wiz Satch just said –

Tattoo No 'buts'. It's an order. Chop the Dragon's head off.

Quiff It only wants a few bushes.

Tattoo Not one petal.

Slight pause.

Bruise So . . . Prince Quiff got the biggest sword he could find and went to the mountains.

Slight pause.

Old Woman Go on.
Bruise (*with Glitter*) Chop-chop!
Glitter (*with Bruise*) Chop-chop!
Quiff If this messes up my quiff, there'll be trouble.

Quiff picks up table leg and starts climbing pile of rubble.

Quiff Dragon!
Old Woman Louder.
Quiff Dragon!
Satchel Louder!
Quiff Dragon! Dragon! Dragon!
Bruise Then he saw something. On top of the mountain. It was very large and . . . made of twigs.
Quiff What is it?
Old Woman You're the one up the mountain.
Quiff . . . A nest.
Bruise Anything inside?
Quiff Eggs.
Old Woman How many?
Quiff Nine.

Child whimpers in Old Woman's ear.

Old Woman Describe them.
Quiff They're huge. All different colours. Glittering. More beautiful than anything I've ever seen.

Child claps approvingly.

Bruise And that's when the Dragon attacked.
Quiff Why?
Bruise Protecting its nest.
Quiff I'm not hurting it.
Satchel Dragon don't know that.
Bruise The Prince stabbed the Dragon.

Quiff Take that!
Bruise The Dragon chased Prince Quiff back down the
mountain.
Quiff Mind my quiff, you Dragon.

Descends rubble.

You can't beat me! Look at my muscles. My stomach.
Six-pack or what?
Glitter Oh, get on with it.

Quiff swings table leg.

Quiff There!
Bruise What you done?
Quiff Chopped its head off.

Picks up a piece of rubble.

See –! Oh, it's a heavy head.
Bruise Take it to the King.

Quiff drops rubble in front of Tattoo.

Quiff Look at it, Dad! Well, you can't. You're blind. But
if you could – why, you'd see the head of the scariest
Dragon ever. But I – yes, me! Prince Quiff! – I fought it
and won. No problem! What a fight it was.
Tattoo You did a good job, son.
Quiff The Dragon didn't stand a chance against my
muscles.
Old Woman But the Prince had to forget the Dragon.
Quiff Why?
Glitter Time to grow up.
Bruise And marry.
Quiff Marry!
Old Woman A Princess!
Glitter . . . Me?
Quiff Who'd want to marry you? Not me!
Glitter And who'd want to marry you? Not me!

Bruise King Tattoo will decide.
Tattoo Get hitched, you two.

Slight pause.
  Glitter takes a step towards Quiff.

Old Woman Closer.

Glitter takes another step.

Old Woman Closer. (*At Quiff.*) You too!

Quiff takes a step.
  Glitter takes a step.
  Eventually, they stand next to each other.

Satchel The Prince and Princess are married!

Throws torn paper like confetti.
  Others cheer and clap.
  Slight pause.

Old Woman Honeymoon!
Glitter (*with Quiff*) Honeymoon?
Quiff (*with Glitter*) Honeymoon?

Slight pause.

Quiff Wotcha, Princess.
Glitter Wotcha, Prince.
Old Woman Kiss!
Glitter (*with Quiff*) Do what?
Quiff (*with Glitter*) Do what?
Satchel Snog time!
Quiff But I don't fancy her!
Glitter And I don't fancy him!
Old Woman It's for the story.

Quiff and Glitter stare at each other awkwardly.
  Gradually they lean towards each other.
  Just as it looks as if they might actually kiss –

46

Glitter The garden!
Quiff Wh . . . what?
Glitter Bit of a make-over, I think.
Quiff The King won't like you changing things.
Glitter I can't think about kissing till I've made this
garden my own. We can have some yellow roses over
there. And some orange ones over here. And just here –
those roses with different-coloured petals.

Slight pause.

Quiff Did I tell you about the Dragon?
Glitter Zillions of times.
Quiff I fought and fought it. My sword went right in his
eye. Yellow jelly spurted out.
Glitter Do you like this rose?
Quiff I stabbed the other eye.
Glitter This rose?
Quiff More yellow jelly?
Glitter What are you playing at? How we gonna move
the story forward if you keep – Oh, you're so . . . so . . .
Quiff Gorgeous?

Glitter squeals in desperation.

Tattoo What's wrong, Princess Glitter?
Glitter I'm not doing it with him!
Quiff (*laughing*) Doing it?
Glitter You've got a mind like a sewer! Oh, I never
wanted to marry.
Old Woman So what do you want?

Slight pause.
Bruise whispers in Glitter's ear.
Glitter looks at Bruise, unsure.
Bruise nods.

Glitter . . . A baby.
Quiff No way!

Bruise So the King went to –
Satchel Wizard Satchel here!
Quiff I don't want a baby.
Tattoo What can be done, Wizard Satchel?
Quiff I don't want a baby.
Old Woman You do!
Quiff I don't!
Bruise (*with Old Woman*) You do!
Glitter (*with Old Woman*) You do!

Slight pause.

Old Woman Why don't you make a mirror, Wizard
Satchel?

Bruise gives mirror to Satchel.

Satchel A mirror! Right! Good idea. Well . . . it's a
magic mirror, obviously. Now . . . what can it do?
Tattoo Don't you know?
Satchel There's lots of spells, you know.

Slight pause.

Got it! Take this mirror to Prince Quiff. When he looks
in it, he'll forget all about the Dragon.

Gives mirror to Tattoo.

Tattoo So . . . what? The Prince has to look into this all
day. That's the spell?
Satchel Got it! Gradually, break off tiny bits of the
mirror. So small the Prince won't see. And keep doing
that till the mirror's all gone. By that time . . . well, the
Prince will have forgotten about the Dragon altogether.
There! How's that?
Tattoo It'll do.
Satchel One more thing. Don't look into the mirror
yourself.
Tattoo I can't! I'm blind!

48

Satchel Then there's no problem.
Bruise So the King took the mirror to the Prince.
Tattoo Look at this! What d'you see, Prince?

Hands mirror to Quiff.

Quiff Wicked!
Glitter What is it?
Quiff Colours and sparkly things.
Satchel And what about your battle with the Dragon?
Quiff Who cares?

Child claps his hands in approval.

Old Woman Very good.
Bruise The King went to the Princess and told her about
the magic mirror.
Tattoo All we've got to do is break off little bits when the
Prince ain't looking. Soon there'll be no mirror. And . . .
well, who knows? You might be able to care for him.
Bruise You've forgotten something.
Tattoo What?
Satchel The warning.

Child whispers in Old Woman's ear.

Old Woman Good boy. Not to look in the mirror.
Bruise So, that night, Princess Glitter broke a tiny piece
from the mirror and looked –
Glitter Oh, wonderful.
Bruise And then – a noise in the sky!
Tattoo What's going on now?
Old Woman A Dragon!
Bruise More than one! Because, when the Prince had
returned from the killing the Dragon, he forgot about
one thing. Guess what?

Child rushes to Bruise and whispers in her ear.

Bruise Oh, clever boy! The nest!

Child whispers in her ear again.

Bruise With eggs. Exactly! And now the Dragons have grown up and . . .

Child sniffs loudly.

Bruise They smell the roses.

Child flaps arms as if flying.

Bruise They're coming to eat the garden.
Old Woman Well done.
Bruise The Dragons are coming.
Old Woman The Dragons are coming.

Child runs arounds flapping arms.

Tattoo Prince! Son! Do something! – Oh, stop looking in the mirror.
Quiff Wicked!
Tattoo Princess!
Glitter Wonderful!
Tattoo Wizard!
Satchel I warned you.
Bruise Before long there was no garden left. The Dragons . . . oh, they ate everything.

Child whispers in Bruise's ear.

Bruise And more?

Child points at Satchel.

Bruise They ate Wizard Satchel.
Quiff Bad luck, Satch!

Child points at Glitter.

Bruise And Princess Glitter.
Quiff Ha! Ha!

Child points at Quiff.

Bruise And Prince Quiff.
Quiff I'm dead again! Help!
Bruise And King Tattoo's eaten?

Childs shakes head.

Bruise Not the King?

Child whispers in Bruise's ear.

Bruise The King lives on. He tells everyone the story.
How he once had everything. And lost it. Because he
wouldn't share his garden.
Old Woman And that's the end?

Child nods.

Old Woman Who's got the mirror?

Glitter holds up mirror.

Old Woman You know what to do.

Glitter puts mirror on fire.
  Child points at Bruise.

Old Woman But . . . she's just told a story.

Child touches Bruise's earring.

Old Woman He wants your earring.

Bruise gives earring to Child.

Glitter Is that a real diamond?
Bruise I don't think so.

Child take earring to Tattoo.
  He grabs Tattoo's hand and leads him to fire.
  Everyone gathers round.
  Slight pause.

*The stories are gradually becoming more and more
like pieces of theatre. Everyone moving around,
miming actions. An ever-more inventive use of objects
in house as props. The use of fire and torches to
increasing dramatic effect.*

Tattoo There was once a . . . Queen.
Bruise Queen Bruise.
Tattoo She lived with her son.
Quiff Prince Quiff.
Tattoo And they lived in a Castle. But this Castle . . .
well, it was very special.
Glitter (*with Satchel*) How?
Satchel (*with Glitter*) How?
Tattoo It . . . it was made of gold and . . . diamond.

Holds up earring.

Glitter (*with Satchel*) Why?
Satchel (*with Glitter*) Why?
Bruise I made it that way.
Quiff What for?
Bruise For you, of course. When you were born – oh,
I was so happy. I wanted to keep you with me for ever.
Safe. So I created this Castle of Treasure. Look at it!
A wonder of the world.
Quiff This place? A wonder?
Bruise Look again! Stained-glass windows.
Quiff That means I can't see outside.
Bruise Why would you want to?

Slight pause.

And the walls are decorated with gold leaf. Images
of trees made of emeralds. Apples of rubies. You see?
Across the ceiling a map of the heavens. A million
diamonds represent the stars. The moon is the purest
silver with craters of mother of pearl. The rising sun a

swirling mixture of gold and platinum. You see? And
across the floor . . . a river made of crushed sapphires.
The ripples are rarest crystal. See?
Quiff It's amazing.
Bruise Oh, let it amaze! Amaze so much you never want
to leave. Look! Your clothes are silk and stitched with
hair from unicorns. And here – let me massage your
temples with this perfume. It takes a million crushed
orchids to produce one drop.

Slight pause.

Happy?
Quiff Yeah.
Bruise And you'll always stay with me.
Quiff Yeah.

Slight pause.

What happened to Dad?
Bruise Wh–what?
Quiff The King! What happened to him?
Bruise I've told you that story a million times.
Quiff Tell it again.

Slight pause.

Bruise A long time ago – before you were born – I wanted
to go to the seaside.
Quiff That's the most beautiful place in Brokenville!
Bruise And the most difficult to get to. But I heard it
had the most beautiful blue coral in the whole world.
Quiff So the King took you.
Bruise That was the plan. But we didn't get very far
though. We got lost in the forest outside the Castle.
Quiff What's a forest like?
Bruise A terrible place.
Quiff Do the trees look like this? Emerald leaves? Ruby
apples?

Bruise Oh, no. Real trees are ugly. And for seven days and nights me and the King – we stumbled around these ugly trees. We didn't know where we were going. The King got so hungry he picked mushrooms and ate them raw.

Quiff Didn't it make the King ill?

Bruise In a way. The next day he started hearing a voice.

Quiff What voice?

Bruise A woman's voice. Or so he said.

Quiff *You* couldn't hear it, then?

Bruise 'You're imagining things,' I told the King. 'I'm not,' says the King. 'The voice wants me to join her in her hut.' 'Then it's a witch!' I told him. 'Cover your ears!'

Quiff Did he?

Bruise No. The next day, I fainted with hunger and exhaustion. When I came round the King had gone. I searched and searched the forest. And then – I saw the Castle. What luck!

Quiff Was the King ever found?

Bruise Eventually. Dead. Birds had pecked out his eyes.

Quiff And – don't tell me! – you were pregnant.

Bruise It must've happened on that last night I was with the King. I mustn't lose my child to the forest, I thought. Not like I lost the King. So I rebuilt the Castle into this wonder. All the treasure in Brokenville went into its making. Just for you! My son!

Quiff Can I see it?

Bruise What?

Quiff The forest.

Bruise No.

Quiff Just once?

Bruise No.

Tattoo But the Prince wanted to see the forest more than anything. He searched for gaps in the golden walls of the Castle.

Quiff None!
Tattoo In the stained-glass windows.
Quiff None!
Tattoo So he decided to make one.

Quiff picks up a fork.

Tattoo He stole a platinum fork from the dinner table.
That night, when the rest of the Castle was sleeping, he
went to a stained-glass window and –
Quiff Broke it!
Glitter That'd wake the Queen.
Old Woman You'll have to grind away the glass.
Glitter To make a spy-hole.
Quiff That'll take ages.
Tattoo For nine years the Prince grinds away at a small
area of glass – no bigger than a thumbprint – until a hole
appears.
Quiff At last!
Tattoo He looks through it.
Quiff . . . Darkness.
Satchel You'll have to wait until morning.
Quiff Hang on! Something's crawling through the hole.
Glitter A spider!
Quiff Oh, it's wonderful! Look at it go! There!
Bruise What's going on?
Quiff . . . Nothing.
Bruise Don't lie to me – Ouch!
Quiff What's happened?
Satchel The spider bit her.
Glitter It's poisonous.
Bruise Who says?
Quiff You look ill.
Bruise I do?
Quiff Best go to bed.

Helps Bruise to bed.

Bruise Don't go to the forest.
Satchel The Queen's getting sicker by the second.
Bruise Don't go to the forest.
Glitter She's motionless.
Bruise Don't go to the –
Old Woman Frozen!

> *Bruise freezes.*
> *Child claps.*

Quiff Open the gates!

> *Takes a step through hole in wall.*

I'm in the forest. It's wicked!
Tattoo He found a dead blackbird.
Quiff Wicked!
Glitter A twig!
Quiff Wicked!
Glitter And he took these wicked things back to the Castle.
Quiff Look, everyone!

> *Comes back into building.*

Queen Bru – she said it was a terrible place outside. But it's not. Look. It's full of treasure.

> *Slight pause.*

I want a cloak made out of . . . dead birds.

> *Child claps.*

Quiff A crown made out of . . . twigs.

> *Child claps more.*

Quiff And I want . . . leaves in my hair. And my skin covered with dirt.

Child claps even more.
  Old Woman joins in.

Old Woman Very good.
Satchel (*with Glitter*) Yes. Very good.
Glitter (*with Satchel*) Well done! Good!

  Slight pause.

Quiff The forest is a wonder of the world. I'm going
to live in it for ever. I'm going to eat squirrels and
mushrooms. Drink rainwater. For the first time in my
life, I'm happy. Really happy.
Bruise Where's my son?
Tattoo Then – to everyone's surprise – the Queen woke
up!
Bruise I'm better now. Prince Quiff! Son!

  Quiff approaches Bruise.

Quiff Wotcha, Queen Bru.
Satchel He wore a cloak of dead birds!
Glitter Crown of twigs!
Satchel Leaves in his hair!
Tattoo Dirt on his skin!
Bruise (*screaming*) Noooooooooooooo!

  Child laughs.
  Slight pause.

Tattoo That night the Queen went to –
Satchel Me again!
Bruise My son is –
Satchel Bonkers!
Bruise What can I do?
Satchel Whatever made him bonkers must be destroyed.
Bruise . . . The forest?
Satchel Bingo!
Bruise Destroy it . . . how?

Satchel Up to you.

Child points to fire.

Bruise Burn it?

Child nods.

Old Woman (*at Bruise*) Do it!

Child takes burning stick from fire and gives it to Quiff.

Quiff Me?
Old Woman Ah, yes. Very good. You!
Quiff But . . . why? I like the forest.
Bruise Do as you're told.

Quiff goes to the window.

Quiff So long, forest.

Throws burning stick out of window.

Tattoo One tree caught fire.
Satchel Another!
Glitter Another!
Bruise Another!
Old Woman Another!
Tattoo Until the whole forest is burning! Burning!

They relax as if the story's over.
  But Child is restless.
  He whispers in Tattoo's ear.

Tattoo The air's full of sparks.
Bruise So . . . what next?

Child rushes to Bruise and whispers in her ear.

Bruise The Castle is burning.
Quiff We can run away.

Child whispers in Quiffs's ear.

Quiff My clothes are burning!

Child whispers in Bruise's ear.

Bruise Mine are too.
Quiff (*with Bruise*) Help!
Bruise (*with Quiff*) Help!

Child whispers in Old Woman's ear.

Old Woman Your skin is burning.
Bruise (*with Quiff*) No!
Quiff (*with Bruise*) No!

*Child is becoming hysterical now.
He is whimpering out loud.*

Old Woman Shush! Calm down.

*Old Woman holds Child.
Others cluster round Child.*

*Gradually Child calms.
Long pause.*

Old Woman (*at Child*) Is this your house?

Child nods.

Quiff What happened to your mum and dad?
Old Woman What happened to any of us? Can any of you remember? No.

Slight pause.

Just tell stories. That's all you can do in this place.

Slight pause.

Brokenville.

Child whispers in Old Woman's ear.

Old Woman Sure?

Child nods.

Old Woman He says, Perhaps something wasn't burnt.
In the last story. Not everything was destroyed.
Tattoo What?

Child whisper in Old Woman's ear.

Old Woman A leaf?
Bruise Just . . . a leaf.
Glitter And that's the end?
Old Woman No. It's the beginning.

Child takes earring from Tattoo and puts it on the fire.

Old Woman Next story, someone.

Glitter breathes into her hands.

Glitter A breath. How's that?

Child nods enthusiastically.

Old Woman Well, I can't wait for this one.
Glitter There was once an ugly Witch.

Everyone looks at the Old Woman.

Old Woman Typical.

Quiff laughs.

Glitter And this ugly Witch fell in love with Prince Quiff.

Quiff stops laughing.

Glitter Every day the witch went to the Prince and said –
Old Woman I've got a beautiful little hut in the forest.
You'd like it if you gave it a chance. I'll cook you my
speciality. Squirrel and mushroom pie. Come on. Give
me a try, Quiffy.

Others laugh.

Quiff Don't call me Quiffy. (*At others.*) Shut it, you lot!

Old Woman approaches Quiff.

Old Woman Kiss me! Kiss me! Kiss me!

Quiff squeals and runs away from her.
Others laugh all the more.
Slight pause.

Glitter The Prince went to King Tattoo and told him about the Witch.

Quiff She's rampant.

Tattoo Oh, I remember her from years ago. In those days . . . the Witch used to live here.

Quiff In the Castle?

Tattoo She used to do magic to entertain us.

Quiff What happened?

Tattoo One day the land was invaded. I begged the Witch to help. Asked her to make . . . a powerful weapon.

Quiff What she say?

Old Woman I'm a good Witch. My magic must not be used to hurt.

Quiff Did the enemy have powerful weapons?

Tattoo They could destroy a whole village.

Snaps fingers.

Like that!

Quiff You should have asked the Witch again.

Tattoo I did.

Quiff What she say?

Old Woman I'm a good Witch. My magic must not be used to hurt.

Quiff So the war dragged on?

Tattoo For years and years.

Quiff We won though?
Tattoo Eventually, yes. But . . . oh, so many wars and battles. Piles of bodies everywhere. People torn apart. Everything broken.
Quiff Hope you taught her a lesson.
Tattoo I banished her.
Quiff That all?
Tattoo What else could I do? (*At Old Woman.*) You'll stay in the forest from now on.

Slight pause.

Quiff (*with Tattoo*) Go on!
Tattoo (*with Quiff*) Go on!

Old Woman moves further away.

Quiff And you stay there, you old bag.
Old Woman Don't you dare call me that.

Slight pause.

You know I love you, gorgeous Quiffy. Come here.

Slight pause.

Please.

Quiff joins Old Woman.

Old Woman I can't sleep for thinking about you. You haunt me, you sexy beast. Your eyes are so . . . oh, look at them. Sparkling. Please . . . let me touch your six-pack stomach.
Quiff No way.
Old Woman Finger?
Quiff No.
Old Woman Hair?
Quiff No.
Old Woman Then . . . oh, I've got it! Yes! Let me hold my hand in front of your lips and feel your breath.

Old Woman looks at Glitter.
   Glitter smiles and nods.

Quiff No way.
Glitter And then, one day, the land was invaded again . . .
Tattoo Prince! Son! Hear that?
Quiff Wh . . . what?
Tattoo Explosions ! Bombs! Sounds like the enemy has got even bigger weapons this time.
Quiff Villages gone –

Snaps fingers.

Like that!
Tattoo Cities too.
Quiff What can we do?
Tattoo No idea.

Slight pause.

Quiff Got it!

Goes to Old Woman

Listen, Witchy, if I let you hold your hand in front of my mouth like you wanted . . . will you make me a really powerful weapon?
Old Woman I'm a good Witch. My magic must not be used to hurt.

Quiff turns to leave.

Old Woman Wait! Let me feel!
Quiff And I'll get a weapon?
Old Woman Yes, yes.

Feels Quiff's breath and lets out an ecstatic cry.

Glitter And so . . . the Witch made the weapon.
Quiff Big explosion! Tons of smoke!
Tattoo Millions of their people are dead.

Quiff Brilliant!
Tattoo But they keep on fighting.
Quiff . . . How come?
Tattoo Their weapons are even more powerful. What can we do?

Slight pause.

Quiff goes to Old Woman.

Quiff Hey! Witchy! If I let you . . . touch my quiff, will you make me a more powerful weapon.?
Old Woman I'm a good Witch. My magic –

Quiff turns to leave.

Old Woman No! Wait! I'll do it! Just . . . oh, let me touch that wicked quiff.
Quiff Don't mess it though.

Old Woman strokes hair and lets out an ecstatic cry.

Glitter The weapon was made.
Quiff King! Dad! Look! Explosions like you've never seen. Boom! Whole areas of ground where nothing will grow for zillions of years.
Tattoo Very impressive.
Glitter But the enemies' weapons are still stronger.
Quiff No way.
Tattoo 'Fraid so – What can we do? Any ideas?
Quiff . . . Bloody hell!

Goes to Old Woman.

If I let you touch my finger –
Old Woman Deal!

Grabs Quiff's finger.

Glitter Victory!

64

Slight pause.

Tattoo What's wrong, son? You look restless.
Quiff Why don't I go back to the Witch and ask her . . .
to make The Most Powerful Weapon of All.
Tattoo The Most Powerful Weapon of All?
Quiff So no one will ever invade us again. A weapon to
end all wars.
Tattoo Good idea. But . . . will she do it?
Quiff She's under my spell. She won't be able to say no.

Quiff goes to Old Woman.

Old Woman Hello, gorgeous.
Quiff If I let you feel my skin, will you make me The
Most Powerful Weapon of All?
Old Woman The Most Powerful Weapon of All? For
feeling your skin? I can't. The price is too high.

Turns to leave.

Quiff Wait! I'll let you touch me anywhere.
Old Woman Anywhere?

Slight pause.

No. I can't.

Turns to leave again.

Quiff I'll let you . . . hold me in your arms.

Slight pause.

I'll let you . . . kiss me.

Slight pause.

With tongues.
Old Woman . . . No. I can't.

Turns to leave.

Quiff I'll take my clothes off. Show you all my muscles. I'll stay the night with you in your hut. And you can do anything you like to me.
Old Woman Anything?
Quiff Anything.
Old Woman Get in that hut!

Slight pause.

Glitter In the morning . . . the Witch had changed. She was no longer old and ugly.
Quiff You're gorgeous too.
Old Woman (*with Glitter*) I know.
Glitter (*with Old Woman*) I know.

Old Woman looks at Glitter, smiles and nods.

Glitter The way I used to look – that was a curse. All I needed was someone to . . . love me.
Quiff I . . . I still need The Most Powerful Weapon of All, you know.
Glitter Of course. But . . . making it will take a little time. And be a bit painful. For me. So . . . until it's made you've got to stay with me in the forest. Deal?
Quiff . . . Deal.

Glitter holds hand out to Quiff.
Slowly – oh, so slowly – he takes it.
They begin strolling around.

Glitter Fancy something to eat?
Quiff Squirrel pie?
Glitter With mushrooms.
Quiff Not hungry.

Slight pause.

Glitter Like your hair.
Quiff You do?
Glitter Suits you.

Quiff Thanks. I . . . I like yours too.
Glitter Really?
Quiff And your eyes.
Glitter My eyes?
Quiff They're . . . shiny. And – look! I can see me in them.

Quiff and Glitter are face to face now, very close.
Perhaps they might kiss.
Slight pause.
Then –

Glitter Ouch!
Quiff What's wrong?
Glitter A pain.
Quiff Where?
Glitter Belly.
Quiff What can I do?
Glitter Help me lie down.

Quiff helps Glitter to the ground.

Quiff Help! Someone! Help! Anyone!
Glitter Don't worry! It's only – Ahhh!
Quiff Only what?
Glitter Look between my legs!
Quiff Do what?

Child rushes to Quiff and whispers in his ear.

Quiff A baby!
Glitter A boy.
Quiff My son.
Glitter Take him to the river.
Quiff He can't swim yet.
Glitter To give him a wash.
Quiff Oh, right. Yeah. Sure.

Goes to puddle.

Get you good and clean, little baby.

Slowly, as Quiff bathes imaginary baby, something changes with him.
    He calms, becomes thoughtful.
    Pause.

Glitter What's wrong?
Quiff Oh . . . nothing.
Glitter Look at his little fingers.
Quiff . . . They're perfect.
Glitter And look – a birthmark on his leg.
Bruise Don't let anyone hurt him.
Quiff I won't.
Bruise Cross your heart?
Quiff Cross my heart.
Bruise And hope to die?
Quiff . . . Yes.
Bruise Say it.

Slight pause.

Old Woman Say it.
Quiff Hope to die.
Glitter Now take it to the King – this baby.
Bruise Your child.
Old Woman And tell him at last, we have made it.
Quiff What?
Glitter (*with Old Woman*) The Most Powerful Weapon of All.
Old Woman (*with Glitter*) The Most Powerful Weapon of All.

Child claps with delight and lifts a shell into the air.

Satchel A shell!
Old Woman (*at Quiff*) Quickly!
Quiff There was once a . . .

68

Takes shell from Child.

A Princess!

There should be a natural fluidity and exhilarating speed to the storytelling now. Movement, use of found objects, torchlight, fire – everything used to create image after image. The evolution from static narration to full blown theatre is now complete.

Glitter Look at my hair. My sparkly eyes. I am perfection.
Quiff Looks ain't everything.
Glitter Wanna snog, Prince?
Quiff . . . No.
Glitter Liar!

Approaches Quiff.

Come on! You know you want to.

Slowly Quiff leans forward.
Just as he's about to kiss Glitter –

Glitter Hang on! We're brother and sister.
Quiff Don't play games.
Glitter *You* do!
Quiff That was before.
Glitter When we were children, you mean.
Quiff I've grown up now.
Glitter Ha!
Quiff I have! I have!
Bruise Don't let her upset you, son.
Quiff She thinks I'm just a joke.
Bruise Your sister thinks everyone's a joke.
Tattoo Including me.
Bruise She's got you wrapped around her little finger.
Tattoo She's such a flirt.
Quiff She flirts with you?

Bruise Haven't you noticed?
Quiff But he's the King. Her dad!
Bruise She's after the Kingdom.
Quiff But . . . if I'm the Prince –
Bruise Brokenville will be yours by right.
Quiff So how can she get it?
Bruise She's a devious one, your sister. Devious! Devious!
Quiff Don't wind yourself up.
Bruise I need an aspirin.
Quiff I'll go down to the beach and find a shell. For your collection. That'll calm you.

> *Quiff searches near puddle.*
> *Glitter approaches and watches him.*

Glitter What you up to?
Quiff Looking for a shell for the Queen.

> *Holds up shell.*

Think she'll like this?
Glitter Who cares?

> *Quiff points.*

Quiff Look!
Glitter . . . What?
Quiff A whale!
Glitter Boring.
Quiff No. They're not.
Glitter Tell me one interesting thing about a whale.
Quiff . . . Wizard Satchel knows interesting things.
Satchel I do?
Glitter I'm waiting.

> *Child whispers in Satchel's ear.*

Satchel Right! How the first whale was made! Ready?
All (*except Child*) Ready!

Satchel A long time ago there were lots and lots of
Wizards. In fact, you couldn't throw a lobster without
hitting one. Anyway . . . one day, just to pass the time,
all these Wizards got together and decided to have a
game. A sort of contest. To see who could change
themselves into the most amazing creature. Lots and lots
of creatures were created that day.

Quiff Like what?

Satchel Creatures with two beaks and a hundred legs.
Creatures with . . . horns that glowed in the dark. There
was even a giant, flying seahorse.

Quiff Where are they now?

Satchel They don't exist.

Quiff Why?

Satchel As soon as a Wizard turned himself into one of
these remarkable creatures he turned himself back again.

Quiff Why?

Satchel He might forget what it was like to be a Wizard.

Quiff Go on.

Satchel One day, a Wizard turned himself into a very big
animal.

Quiff A whale!

Satchel All the other Wizards cheered and clapped.
They'd never seen such a remarkable creature. A few of
them got carried away and turned themselves into whales
too. They swam and splashed in the sea. Dived down
to shipwrecks. Then swam up, faster and faster. Until –
whooosh! They shot out of the ocean. Then crashed back
down – splasshhh! – sending waves all over the place.
They enjoyed being whales so much they forgot how to
change themselves back into Wizards. And then . . . well,
they forgot they'd ever been Wizards at all.

Quiff What a wonderful story.

Slight pause.

Glitter What you doing now?

Quiff Skimming stones across the ocean. Look! See that one bounce! One! Two! Three! Four! Nearly reached that bit of blue coral. It's so beautiful and . . . pure. That's my ambition you know. To reach blue coral.
Glitter You really have changed.

Walks away.

Quiff Come back!
Glitter Hear the Prince, Dad?
Tattoo What's wrong with him?
Glitter Wants me to stay on the beach.
Tattoo Why don't you?
Glitter He wants to . . . kiss me.
Tattoo Such an affectionate brother.
Glitter He doesn't want that sort of kiss.
Tattoo What you getting at?
Glitter Oh, not now, Dad. Running away from the Prince has tired me out.
Tattoo Running away?
Glitter I'm going to my room.

Glitter sits on bed.
    Quiff and Glitter look at each other.
    Slight pause.

Glitter Did you hit it?
Quiff What?
Glitter Blue coral.
Quiff It's too far.
Glitter Keep practising.

Slight pause.

Quiff You look a bit sad.
Glitter Oh . . . do I?

Quiff sits next to Glitter.
    Slight pause.

Quiff What's wrong?

Glitter It's . . . difficult to put into words.

Quiff Try.

Glitter Well . . . it's just that sometimes I feel like I'm the wrong character in the right story.

Quiff And sometimes the right character in the wrong story. But never –

Glitter (*with Quiff*) The right character in the right story.

Quiff (*with Glitter*) The right character in the right story.

They lean close to each other.

Glitter Perhaps the answer is . . . to be ourselves.

Quiff In our own story.

Glitter Whatever the story is.

Quiff Whoever we are.

They lean closer.
    Closer.
    Then –

Tattoo What you two up to?

Quiff (*with Glitter*) Dad!

Glitter (*with Quiff*) Dad!

Tattoo You're brother and sister!

Glitter The Prince forced his way into my bedroom.

Tattoo Did you?

Quiff No way!

Glitter Liar!

Tattoo I'm fed up with you pestering your sister.

Glitter Banish him!

Tattoo I will.

Glitter Go on, then.

Tattoo You're banished.

Quiff Mum!

Bruise What's going on?

Glitter The King's banished Prince Quiff.
Bruise He can't do that.
Glitter If you don't like it, he'll banish you too.
Bruise Wouldn't dare.
Glitter Dad?
Tattoo You're banished!
Bruise Goodbye, then.
Glitter Goodbye.
Quiff Goodbye.
Glitter Goodbye.

Bruise and Quiff walk a bit further.

Glitter Keep going.

Bruise and Quiff walk outside the building.

Glitter Help me put this sharktooth necklace on, Dad.

Picks up piece of string and hands it to him.

How do I look?
Tattoo Very tasty.
Bruise You're her dad, don't forget.

Slight pause.

Glitter Can I have all Queen Bruise's jewellery?
Tattoo Don't see why not.
Glitter And Prince Quiff's weapons?
Tattoo Anything you want.
Glitter Anything?
Tattoo Anything.
Glitter The sun.
Tattoo . . . What?
Glitter Well, just a piece of it. A sunbeam. Get me one.
Tattoo But . . . how?
Glitter Ask Wizard Satchel.

Tattoo approaches Satchel.

74

Satchel So you want to catch a –
Quiff He ain't told you yet.
Satchel I'm a Wizard, dickhead!

Slight pause.

I'll make you a giant flying seahorse.
Tattoo I don't want a –
Satchel You can ride this giant flying seahorse up to the sky. Catch a sunbeam. Then give it to the Prince.
Tattoo It's for the Princess.
Satchel Then the answer's no.
Tattoo What d'you mean?
Satchel The Princess finds my stories boring. I wouldn't piddle on her if she was burning.
Tattoo You're banished.
Satchel Goodbye.
Tattoo Goodbye.

Slight pause.

I'll . . . I'll get someone else to help me – You're a Witch, right?
Old Woman Thought everyone had forgotten me.
Tattoo I need a giant flying seahorse.
Old Woman Why?
Tattoo If you're a Witch, you should know.
Old Woman You're right. Forget it!
Tattoo Make it or I'll have you . . . fed to piranhas.
Old Woman All right, I'll make it. But be careful. Catching a sunbeam is dangerous. Better men than you have been burnt to a crisp.
Tattoo Just make it.
Old Woman It's behind you.
Tattoo . . . Where?
Old Woman There!
Tattoo Where?
Old Woman Giant flying seahorses are invisible.

Tattoo Princess Glitter! I'm ready to catch the sunbeam.
Glitter Up you go.
Tattoo A kiss before I go.
Glitter A kiss when you get back.

Slight pause.

Tattoo I'm sitting on the seahorse now.
Glitter Get a move on.

Tattoo is unsure what to do.
    Slight pause.

Glitter What you waiting for?

Tattoo is still unsure what to do.
    Slight pause.

Suddenly Child has an idea.
    He runs around the house searching for something.
    Finally, in a box full of party stuff, he finds a mirrorball.
    He holds it above his head.

The others aim their torches at the mirrorball.
    Light refracts everywhere.

Tattoo Sunbeam!

Tattoo starts chasing Child.
    Child is laughing, enjoying every moment of it.
    Others laugh and cheer.
    Much joy and play.

Finally, Child is cornered.
    Tattoo takes mirrorball from Child.

Tattoo Gotchya!

Takes mirrorball to Glitter.

Glitter Wonderful!

76

Tattoo Kiss?
Glitter Later! I want to put my sunbeam in this shell.

Picks up shell.

My glowing crown!

Tattoo clutches chest.

Tattoo Aaahh! My heart!
Glitter Look at me wearing my crown.
Tattoo Won't somebody help me?
Old Woman Told you the sunbeam was a bad idea.

Helps Tattoo over to bed.

Tattoo Is the Princess happy?
Old Woman Delirious.
Tattoo That's all that matters.

Lies on bed.

Old Woman Comfortable?
Tattoo Not really.
Old Woman I can't help that.

Slight pause.

Tattoo I don't want to die.
Old Woman Can't help that either.
Tattoo I . . . I want a kiss.

Old Woman bends towards Tattoo.

Tattoo Not from you! The Princess!
Old Woman Princess!
Glitter What?
Old Woman Feel like kissing the King?
Glitter No.
Old Woman It might save him.
Glitter I'm busy.
Old Woman Doing what?

77

Glitter Wearing the crown. Everyone falls to their knees when they see me.
Old Woman That's the sunbeam. Not you.
Glitter Shut up. Or I'll have you fed to piranhas
Old Woman She won't come, King.
Tattoo I only want a bloody kiss.
Old Woman You're looking sicker by the second, I'm afraid.
Tattoo One kiss –
Old Woman The King is dead.
Glitter Long live the Queen!
Others Long live the Queen!
Glitter Right. Now then . . . Yes! We've got to bury the poor old King. We'll do it at sea. Could do with a boat trip.

Gently sways from side to side as if on a boat.

Gradually, others join in.
Slight pause.

Glitter Look! A whale!
Satchel It's me! Wizard Satchel. I've changed myself into a whale. Splash, splash!
Old Woman Look! The water's put out your sunbeam.
Glitter My crown!
Old Woman Now everyone can see you for what you really are.

Old Woman and Satchel close in on Glitter.
Glitter backs away.
Closer.
Closer.
Then –

Child Stop!

They all look at Child.
Slight pause.

78

Old Woman Stop?
Child The story mustn't end like this.
Old Woman Finish it for us, then.

Slight pause.

Child The whale – it splashes the boat.
Old Woman Yes?
Child The shell – it rolls across the deck.
Satchel Good.
Child The Princess chases after it.

Slight pause.

Go on, then.
Glitter Do I catch it?
Child You fall overboard.
Glitter Not drown?
Child No.
Glitter Splash, splash.
Child The whale – Yes! That's it. The whale swallows you up.
Glitter Eaten?
Child No.
Glitter I'm . . . in the whale's belly.
Child I think you'd be scared.
Glitter I'm going to die!
Child Are you sorry for what you did to the Prince?
Glitter Yes.
Child And for what you did to the Queen?
Glitter Yes.
Child So they're not banished any more?
Glitter No.
Child (*at Quiff and Bruise*) Come back, you two!

Quiff and Bruise approach.

Child Now all we need is a feather.
Old Woman Why?

Child I'm going to tickle the whale's nose.
Satchel I'm going to sneeze.
Child Sneeze out the Princess.
Satchel Ah–tishoo!
Glitter I'm alive!
Child Now kiss the King.

> *Slight pause.*

He's not thrown overboard yet, is he?
Old Woman No.
Child Then give him that bloody kiss.

> *Glitter kisses Tattoo.*
> *Tattoo sits up.*

Tattoo I'm alive!
Glitter Oh, forgive me. Everyone. Please. Forgive.

> *Pause.*

Child Last story, everyone.

> *Child sits by fire.*
> *Others gather round him.*

Child There was once a child – Me! He was very scared.
And he met some people. And they . . . told him stories
about –
Old Woman Witches.
Satchel Wizards.
Bruise Queens.
Tattoo Kings.
Quiff Princes.
Glitter Princesses.
Child And now . . . I'm not scared any more.

> *Blackout.*

THE PILGRIMAGE

Paul Goetzee

Characters

Granpa Grimm, Gregor's father, a shepherd
Mermer, Clove's mother
Clove, wife of Gregor
Gregor, a shepherd
Brag, a shepherd, brother to Gregor
Butt, eldest son of Clove and Gregor, shepherd
Lena, wife of Butt
Chaff, daughter of Clove and Gregor
Mendel, daughter of Clove and Gregor,
Chaff's twin sister
Josef, a goatherd
Sylvian, the man who lives in the trees
Virgin of the Shepherds
Virgin of the Goatherds

The Chorus

The Pilgrimage is set in a fictitious,
possibly Eastern European country,
in a wild and rugged landscape that can only
support sheep and goats. The music is the music
of Turkey, Armenia and the Balkans.

The time is the past, the present,
but hopefully not the future.

Note: in a small-cast production,
the Chorus' lines can be spoken be Sylvian

*Music: a wild and haunting theme, ominous and
threatening, which breaks into something more
rhythmic, against which the Chorus say their lines:*

Chorus
  This is the mountain
  These are the valleys where
  Sheep and goats tear thistles
  And dry grass
  From the dust and stones
Clove I never thought it would happen to our family.
Gregor Things like this only happen to other people.
Chaff and Mendel Not to us.
Chorus
  One hundred years ago
  A woman appeared on the mountain
  To three shepherd girls
  Minding their flocks
  She touched the twisted foot
  Of one of them and made it straight
  She told them terrible secrets
  And vanished
Mermer People have long memories.
Grimm As long as time.
Butt People's memories are short.
Lena It all depends on what you want to remember.
Chorus
  The people of these hills
  Made a shrine on the mountain
  It became

A place of pilgrimage
To this shrine came a group
Of pilgrims
Clothed in shame

Brag Nobody is innocent. All blood must be paid for.
Mermer It is that simple.
Brag A family must stand by its own.
Grimm Or it will destroy itself.
Chorus
  Hear their story

The family take their positions: Mermer is carried on Clove's back. Clove has two stirrups hanging from her waist into which Mermer puts her feet. Gregor carries Grandpa Grimm in the same way. Mendel and Chaff are bound together at the wrist by a red cord. Brag wears an axe or machete in his belt. Butt wears spectacles and always carries a book, which he sometimes rests on Lena's back to read.

Chorus
  Take the seedling memory
  Plant it in anger
  Water it with bitter tears
  Nurse it with fear
  And watch it
  Blossom into hatred

The family breaks up and brings on a rough wooden table to which are fastened plates. Stools and/or benches are brought on for them to sit down.

Clove Food! Grandpa Grimm! Mendel, Chaff, Butt, Lena, Gregor, Brag!
Mermer Come and eat now. Or starve!
Chorus The family that eats together
  Will not eat each other

So goes the proverb
In these mountains
Gregor (*entering with Grimm on his back*) I could eat a horse.
Clove Horse is off. It's mutton.
Gregor It's always mutton.
Mermer Mutton is good. Sheep is good.

Butt and Lena enter. He is reading a book using her as a reading stand.

Lena Haven't you finished that book yet?
Butt Last chapter, my sweet.
Lena Why do you read such big books?
Butt Because I like them. Books are knowledge. Knowledge is power. Power is an aphrodisiac. An aphrodisiac is an aid to sexual enjoyment. Ergo, books are sexy!
Mermer You are about as sexy as a whelk, Butt. Now, put that book down before I throw it on the fire!
Butt Yes, Mermer.
Mermer I was just saying.
Lena What were you just saying, Mermer?
Grimm She was just saying that sheep is good.
Brag (*entering in a bloodstained apron*) Sheep is life.
Butt If you say so, Brag.
Clove Wait! Where are the twins?
Brag On the slopes watching my sheep.
Mermer Plotting insolence and making mischief, more like.
Gregor Double trouble.
Butt Trouble squared to be precise. Their trouble-making increases exponentially by a factor of the sum of their number, that is to say . . . two.

A pause as they look at Butt.

Mermer Butt, eat your mutton before your head explodes.

Butt Yes, Mermer.

Mendel and Chaff enter.

Clove Where have you been?

Mendel Half a dozen of Uncle Brag's ewes went charging up the southern pass.

Chaff It took us ages to get them back.

Brag You didn't lose any, did you?

Chaff Of course not.

Mendel What do you think we are, stupid goatherds?

Chaff Sybil just had two beautiful lambs.

Clove I know, they're hanging in the larder.

Chaff Oh mother! They're only babies.

Grimm Babies make the tenderest meat.

Gregor May the Lord make us truly thankful for that which gives us our food and clothing: the blessed sheep.

All Amen.

Mendel Sylvian the treeman says he's seen goats on the western slopes.

Grimm Ignore him. He's as mad as my trousers.

Clove You shouldn't be talking to him.

Chaff He says he saw a herd passing by only yesterday.

Gregor We will have no goatherds here!

Clove Gregor, calm down.

Brag If he's right, we will have to drive them out. They will ruin us.

Mermer Remember the last time goats came to the valleys.

There is a long pause.

Chaff Of course we don't remember. We're not old like you.

Gregor Then listen. Let your grandmother pour vintage
wine into fresh gourds. (*He taps the twins on the
head.*)

Mendel and Chaff Ow!

Mermer The last time goatherds came to our mountains,
I was a little girl of seven. They came and drove out
all the sheep.

Chorus
Drove them out.

Mermer They rounded them up, slaughtered them and
burnt them in huge fires.

Chorus
Fire!

Grimm I was ten. I remember them taking my father's
sheep and hacking them to pieces.

Chorus
Hacked them to pieces.

Grimm They gave me and my brothers roast kid to eat.
They forced us to eat unclean meat.

Chorus
Unclean!

Grimm I wouldn't, so they beat me. I ran away from
them. They burned down my father's farm.

Chorus
Burning.

Grimm Slaughtered his flocks.

Chorus
Slaughter!

Mermer We have our memories. Now they are yours.

Grimm Memory is a gift to pass on to your children.

Lena Memory is a curse too.

Gregor Quiet!

Butt But, didn't we go into their mountains and burn all
their goats in revenge?

Grimm Of course we did. It's expected.

Mermer They started it.

Butt But . . .

Gregor But but but! Your head is full of buts.

Mendel That's why we call him Butt!

Butt But . . . but . . .

Mendel and Chaff start head-butting each other.

Mendel and Chaff But but but but but but! Ow!

Butt But!

Clove But what Butt?

Butt All I was going to say was that before the goatherds came to our mountains, we went to theirs and slaughtered all their goats.

Mermer That was a crusade!

Butt Against goats?

Gregor Against the unclean.

Butt So they didn't start it. We did.

Mermer No. Before that they came here and killed all our sheep.

Gregor Why are you saying all this anyway, Butt?

Lena Butt likes to study history.

Brag From books? What use are books? People who read books shouldn't keep sheep.

Lena Butt is a good shepherd – even if he does wear glasses.

Butt What?

Brag So how come he lost that ram down a gully the other week? Good breeding stock too. Balls on him like church bells. The ram I mean, not Butt.

Mermer Ram's balls in a dill sauce. That was a treat when I was a girl.

Gregor History is one thing, Butt. Memory another. You can say anything in a book. Tell lies, twist the truth. And because it's written down people will believe it. But it's what we hold inside our heads that matters.

That is pure and unchanging. We pass on our
memories in our songs and our stories.
Chaff So what do we do when the goatherds come?
Mermer We defend ourselves!
Grimm To the death!
All (*stabbing their knives into the table, Butt, Lena and Chaff not too sure*) To the death!
Grimm Now carve that mutton, Gregor, before we all die of hunger!
Chorus (*during which the cast clear the table and seating*)
    This is our family
    Our happy family
    Bound together in common purpose
    Tied with ropes of love
    Sharp words are spoken
    But wounds soon healed
    Blows exchanged for
    Kindness and embraces
Chorus
    Nothing is a secret in our family
    Nothing so dark it cannot be spoken
    All wrongs can be forgiven
    All hurt soothed

Chaff and Mendel are minding the sheep.
   Sylvian, the man who lives in trees, swings down from branches overhead, hanging upside down as he talks to them. He begins by throwing acorns at them. At first, the girls ignore him, then it gets too much.

Mendel Ow! Stop that, you freak!
Sylvian Make me.
Chaff Stop acting the goat, Sylvian. We shouldn't even be talking to you.
Sylvian No, Sylvian is the bogie man, isn't he? The loon in the laburnum.

Mendel That's not a laburnum.

Sylvian How would you know? It hasn't got four legs and a fleece, so you wouldn't have a clue.

Chaff Get lost, treeman.

Sylvian Tell me something –

Mendel No.

Sylvian Why are you two always joined together?

Mendel Because we're twins.

Chaff We were born this way.

Mendel Blood flows along this cord.

Chaff And back again. Anyway, what's it to you?

Sylvian The goatherds are coming.

Mendel So you said.

Chaff We still don't believe you.

Sylvian I'm glad I don't herd sheep any more.

Chaff You don't do anything any more.

Mendel You just live in a tree and talk goat-shit.

Sylvian My mother always said: Sylvian, make sure you keep both feet on the ground.

Mendel But you don't keep your feet on the ground.

Sylvian My father always said: never listen to your mother.

Chaff Have you never come down?

Sylvian Never.

Mendel Isn't it uncomfortable?

Sylvian Not any more. I got used to it. Besides I can be above the everyday. Think my own thoughts.

Chaff Eat leaves.

Sylvian To suck the meat from a warm thrush's egg – paradise! It's not a bad life.

Mendel Our grandma said you were put up there as a punishment.

Sylvian Well, maybe your dear old gran is right. I'm a criminal. That's why I live in a tree. This is my prison. My hell. My heaven. There's going to be more burning and slaughtering soon. But it won't concern

me. Up here. I shall just witness all and weep.
(*Laughs.*) See you later! (*He swings back into the tree
and disappears.*)

Mendel Mad.

Chaff Completely mental.

*Josef, a goatherd, enters. He is carrying a kid in his
arms.*

Josef Hello.

Mendel Who are you?

Chaff You're not from round here.

Josef No. I'm lost. Have you anything to eat? I can pay.

Mendel We don't share food with strangers.

Chaff Until we know why they're here.

Josef I'm a herdsman.

Chaff We're all herdspeople.

Mendel Where are your sheep?

Josef I don't herd sheep.

Mendel What do you herd then, chickens?

Josef Goats.

Chaff and Mendel Goats!

Chaff Are you a bit retarded? Don't you know what we
do to goatherds round here?

Josef Yes . . . but I'm hungry.

Chaff Stay there. (*She takes Mendel to one side.*) Mendel,
what should we do?

Mendel Right. I know. We give him some food and some
water. Have a laugh and a joke, wait till he falls
asleep, then pick up a really big stone and drop it on
his head.

Chaff Then what?

Mendel Kill all his goats.

Chaff He looks quite nice . . .

Mendel He's a goatherd, a monster.

Chaff He doesn't look like a monster.

Mendel So what? He's dangerous.

Josef I can let you have this newborn kid for some food and something to drink. Look. (*He shows them the kid.*)

Chaff Ah, isn't it cute? I've never seen a kid before.

Mendel Ugh, it's horrible! Look at its eyes. Like the devil. Don't touch it, Chaff, it's unclean.

Chaff picks up the kid.

Chaff! It's wrong!

Chaff What do you call him?

Josef I don't call him anything.

Chaff That's not very imaginative.

Mendel Goatherds aren't, it's well known. They're stupid. They fall asleep as soon as it goes dark and they have to write L and R on their boots so they know which way to put them on.

Josef We have sheep-people jokes like that.

Chaff He hasn't got L and R on his boots.

Josef That's because it's worn off.

Mendel See!

Chaff I think he's joking. Aren't you?

Mendel Goatherds don't joke. They haven't got a sense of humour like us.

Chaff Where do you come from?

Josef From the south.

Chaff What's it like? In the south.

Mendel Chaff, why are you talking to him?

Chaff Mendel, shut up will you?

Mendel I'm going back to tell our dad. Then you're dead, goatboy.

Chaff You can't go back without me.

Mendel Exactly. At least one of us knows the right thing to do. You've got to come with me.

Chaff No, I want to talk to him. I want to know about the south.

Mendel I'm going without you then.

Chaff No, I'm staying!
Mendel Ow! You'll get a beating.

They start to pull backwards and forwards on the cord.

Chaff That's my problem. I want to stay!
Mendel We've always done everything together.
Chaff Maybe it's time for a change.
Mendel (*pulling out her knife*) All right! If you won't
   come with me, I'll cut the cord. I mean it. I will!
Chaff You wouldn't dare!
Mendel I'm not going to stay with this unclean.
Chaff He's not unclean.
Mendel I'll cut it, Chaff. See if I don't.
Chaff Go on, I dare you.
Mendel What?
Chaff I dare you. Well, what are you waiting for?
Josef Please, there's no need for this –
Mendel Stay out of this, goatface! You've got to the
   count of three, Chaff. One –
Chaff Mendel, think –
Mendel Two –
Chaff You'll regret it.
Mendel Come back with me.
Chaff No!
Mendel Three!

> *Mendel cuts the cord. They both scream, then look at
> each other in horror. Mendel says nothing but runs
> away. Exit.*

Chorus
   The cord has been cut
   The bond of family broken
   Blood spilled
   The bitter truth is spoken:
   Things can never be the same again.
Chaff What have I done?

The family reassembles. At the centre, Gregor holds up the arms of Chaff and Mendel.

Gregor What have you done?

Clove Chaff, Mendel. Answer your father. What have you done?

Mendel She wanted to stay with the goatherd.

Mermer Wicked child! Consorting with the unclean!

Chaff He wasn't unclean.

Grimm He stank of goats. It never leaves them.

Chaff We stink of sheep.

Gregor Shut up, the lot of you!

Brag enters still in his bloodstained apron, but this time holding a bloodstained cleaver in his hand.

Brag There! It's done.

Mermer Did you slaughter every last one?

Brag Every last one.

Grimm And are they burning?

Brag You can see the smoke for miles.

Chaff What about the goatboy? What have you done to him?

Brag He's been taken care of.

Chaff What have you done with him!

Brag He wouldn't tell us where the other herders were.

Chorus

   So we tied him to a tree
   And gutted and jointed him
   With our knives and axes
   His screams filled the quiet valley
   And echoed off the mountain
   The crows pluck at his eyes
   The fox sniffs the bloody entrails
   Flies hum a death-song
   Above his lips
   Murder!

Chaff You killed him!

Brag And if I did? So what?

Gregor Listen to me, Chaff. You are in serious trouble
  already. That mad treefreak, Sylvian, lost the use of
  his legs after he traded with goatherds. They were
  smashed with stones. That is why he lives in trees
  swinging by his arms like an ape. If anyone finds out
  you spoke to a goatherd, the same will happen to you.

Chaff Then let it! Anything is better than living another
  day in this place!

Chaff runs out. Exit.
  *The Chorus gasps and it divides into two. The
  family also divides: Butt, Lena, Clove on one side;
  Grimm, Gregor, Brag, Mermer on the other.*

Chorus
  The bond is cut
  The family split
  The strong chain snaps
  Outrage follows hard upon
  Outrage

Mountainside.
  *A body lies covered with a bloodstained sheet.
  Chaff enters carrying the kid.*

  When black clouds fill the oceans
  And the sun pours down freezing rain
  When the lightning fork strikes upward
  Then will end all pain

*If this is done as a song, Chaff would join in.
  Sylvian appears from the branches.*

Sylvian I saw them do it, you know. Here. Against this
  tree. I covered him with the sheet.

Chaff Treeman, what can I do?

Sylvian Oh, it's 'Treeman what can I do', now is it? Not
'Get lost you loony leaf-eater'?

Chaff I'm in trouble and I've never felt so bad before.
I feel as if I've cut off a part of my own body.

Sylvian Join the club. No one likes people to act on their
own. It makes them look sheepish.

Chaff They told me about you. About what they did to
you.

Sylvian Did you feel sorry for me?

Chaff A bit.

Sylvian I tell you what I did.

Chaff What?

Sylvian Prayed to the Virgin for a miracle. A new set
of legs.

Chaff Did it work?

Sylvian No. But this is where the Virgin appears.

Chaff A hundred years ago.

Sylvian I see her every day picking daisies.

Chaff Don't lie.

Sylvian It's true, I swear. Pray to her. Ask her to bring
your goatboy back to life. It's worth a try.

Chaff He didn't look like a bad person.

Sylvian What did you expect: cloven feet and long curly
horns?

Chaff He came from mountains just like ours. He would
have seen the same sunrise, the same stars, breathed
the same air. Virgin, if you are here and you can hear
me. Help me. Bring the goatherd back to life. I'll do
anything if I can see him whole again. (*Pause, she
waits.*) There: nothing.

Sylvian Wait!

*Music: the Chorus parts and the Virgin emerges from
them carried on high. They set her down.*

Chorus
She appears not as a lady

But as a peasant girl
Her flesh and bones
The ragged yearnings
Of the desperate and the poor
She is made out of wishes
And needs and desires
Gossamer as daydream
Mountainous as prayer
Healer and carer
Open our hearts
Touch the stricken
Breathe life into
The lifeless

Chaff It's her!

Virgin Your name's Chaff, isn't it?

Chaff How did you know?

Virgin Did you expect me not to know? I'd be something of a disappointment if I didn't know your name. What can I do for you?

Chaff Can you bring the goatboy back to life? He's dead.

Virgin (*looking under the sheet*) And in more than one piece by the look of it. You're looking at a big job, sunshine. It'll cost you.

Chaff How much?

Virgin More than you'll want to pay.

Chaff I'll pay it. Anything.

Virgin There is another problem.

Chaff What?

Virgin He's goat. I only do sheep.

Chaff But aren't you the Virgin for all people?

Virgin What books have you been reading? They've got their own Virgin.

Chaff But you'd be doing it for me. A sheep-person.

Virgin Hm. Bit of a theological nicety, but I can roll with that one. Just this once. OK, here goes. Let sinew bond with bone, gristle with offal blah blah blah . . . that should do it. Right, I'm off. Remember, there's a price. There always is.

The Virgin merges back into the Chorus and they carry her away.

There is movement beneath the sheet, then Josef appears.

Sylvian What did I tell you?

Chaff He's alive! You're alive! It was the Virgin. She did it! She brought you back to life!

Josef Murderer! Murderers! Filthy sheep herders! All the stories about you are true!

Chaff No, you've got it wrong. The Virgin brought you back to life!

Josef The Virgin of the goatpeople?

Chaff No . . . not exactly . . . our Virgin . . . but she did a good job.

Josef Blasphemy! No phoney saint of yours could do anything for me.

Chaff But you're alive. You were dead.

Josef Who says?

Sylvian Look, goatsbrains, your head was six feet away from your body and your guts were all over the slopes before I tidied you up. Not many people survive that kind of minor injury, do you know what I'm saying?

Josef Goatpeople are tough. Indestructible.

Sylvian Do you ever get the feeling you're on to a loser with some people?

Josef Give me that kid. It is all that is left of my herd. I am returning to my people and I will tell them what you did to me and to my goats. Then we'll see.

Chaff No, don't go! This wasn't supposed to happen, oh no!

Josef goes. Exit.

Sylvian What did you expect? Violins? A fairy-tale
  ending? His eternal gratitude maybe?
Chaff But it was a miracle. You saw it. He just thinks he
  survived. He must believe he's superhuman.
Sylvian Next thing, he'll be gathering a cult-following
  and letting them kill themselves for him.
Chaff What do I do now, treeman?
Sylvian Suffer. It's the way.
Chaff Thanks.
Sylvian You're welcome. Cuckoo's egg? No? More for
  me then. Cheerio.

Sylvian goes. Exit.

Chorus
  And the goatherd walked back
  Boldly through the valley
  Holding the bleating kid in his arms
  The shepherds stared at him
  In disbelief
  Mouths on hinges
  Children clutching at their mothers' skirts
  Men glowered over closed gates
  This was a dead man
  Breathing air, treading earth underfoot
  Smiling a crooked smile
  At the fear on their faces
  Devil's work
  The goatherd went back to his people
  And told his story.

*The family sets up the table and seating over the
Chorus.*
  *Clove brings in a soup tureen. She carries Mermer
on her back. Gregor carries Granpa Grimm. Butt and
Lena enter, then Brag carrying Mendel, who looks
very ill.*

Chorus
> Home
> Sheltering thatch
> Four stone walls
> Strong fences
> A gate that locks
> Wood burns in the hearth
> The family gathers
> But the house is unquiet
> Like a disturbed graveyard.

Clove Mutton soup anyone? No? No one? Very well, I'll give it to the pigs.

Gregor I'm not hungry.

Butt Nor me.

Lena Me neither.

Mermer You don't know what it's like to starve! Give me the tureen.

Clove gives her the tureen and ladle and she drinks the soup from it as she speaks.

Mermer They say he walked down the valley bold as a horse's buttocks.

Grimm Dark magic.

Brag I saw him die.

Gregor With our own hands, we killed him.

Mermer This is the work of Satan.

Butt Mermer, he came back from the dead.

Mermer Exactly!

Butt If that had happened to a shepherd, we'd be calling it a miracle and declaring him our saviour.

Grimm But he isn't a shepherd, so it must be the work of the devil. Proof!

Mermer He will return with an army. There will be terrible slaughter.

Gregor It will be a proving ground.

Brag A test of honour and courage.

Mermer A second crusade.

Grimm A cleansing.

Clove Is it true that Chaff prayed to the Virgin to bring back the goatherd?

Grimm As true as these trousers. It's all over the market place.

Mermer Shame on her!

Gregor Tha's enough. She's still my daughter!

Mendel My sister . . . a traitor.

Clove Mendel, how dare you!

Mermer Death to all nonbelievers! Death to all the unclean herders of Satan's children! Victory to the pure! Is there any more soup?

Clove No.

Butt I think you're getting this a little out of perspective.

Lena Butt, don't –

Butt She had no choice. She only wanted to talk to the boy and for that she was punished. Call me a simpleton, but it seems a little extreme to me.

Brag Butt, you're a simpleton. Let me ask you something.

Butt If it's about borrowing my complete works of Shakespeare, the answer's no, Brag.

Brag Don't try to be funny, Butt. Are you part of this family?

Butt Of course I am.

Brag Do you believe we should stick together no matter what?

Butt That all depends, you see –

Brag Answer the question, Butt. Do you or don't you? I'm waiting for an answer, Butt. We're all waiting. Well?

Lena What is so bad about people who herd goats instead of sheep? They're poor, like us. They try to scratch a living, like us. Are they so different?

Mermer Blasphemy!

Grimm Outrage!

Mermer Send for the priest! Cut out her tongue!

Clove Mermer, Granpa. Please. This isn't helping anybody. My daughter has cut herself off from this family.

Mermer Then she must answer to the consequences.

Brag I'm still waiting for an answer, Butt.

Butt Lena is right. We are the same people. That is all there is to it.

Lena How can we change what we feel? What we know is right?

Brag Easy. Do as you're told.

Butt We will not. We will do as our hearts tell us.

Brag What your books tell you, you mean!
This is what I found in Butt's cottage. It's a book.

Butt Surprised you recognised it, Brag.

Brag (*holding up a book*) It's about a shepherd who is so corrupt he sells his sheep for twice as many goats and then disguises all the goats as sheep. Everyone believes he is the Good Shepherd and follows him.

Gregor Butt and Lena, leave this house immediately!

Butt It's only a story.

Gregor It's a slur on all good shepherds. Pack your things and leave this valley!

Mendel No! Mother, you can't let him do that!

Mermer You be quiet, or you'll join your sister!

Clove Mermer, don't say that!

Mermer I will say it, and you will listen, daughter! Do you hear me?

Clove I hear you. But I swear I will not be a burden to my daughters. When you die, Mermer, I will burn these stirrups.

Mermer (*digging in her heels hard*) Quiet! These stirrups are passed down through the family. I carried my mother on my back, as she did hers. I gave them to you on your wedding day.

Grimm Listen to your elders, Clove. They have eyes into the past. They can see a pattern which you cannot.

Chorus
 The pattern is a deep-dyed red
 And it streams through time
 Like a fresh kill on the wind

Gregor Leave us, Butt and Lena. Before our anger gets the better of us. Your cottage and your herds are forfeit, as is all your property. You have transgressed all we believe in. My heart is broken, my family torn in two. Go!

Mermer, Brag, Grimm Go!

Chorus Once the wound is dealt
 It never heals
 The blood flows
 In spate
 Like a river after winter snow

Brag brings on a sack filled with books. He empties the books into a stone hearth.

 Homes are pulled down
 Livelihoods destroyed
 Knowledge lost
 In a dawn of scattered ashes

Lena and Butt are expelled from their home like Adam and Eve from paradise. They watch the red glow as the books burn.

 Our only link with the past
 The memories of old men and women
 Whose aged minds preserve
 Hate and fear and anger
 Like wasps in vinegar

Clove goes to comfort Mendel, but Mermer pulls her arm away.

Brag stands with Grimm and Gregor as they oversee Butt and Lena's expulsion.

Chorus
> When the child asks:
> Why so much hate?
> Her elders answer:
> It has always been so
> She asks:
> Will it always be so?
> They answer:
> The pattern is deep-dyed red
> And it streams through time
> Like a fresh kill on the wind

Music: fast, percussive, discordant.
Over the music, the Chorus move/dance, dividing reuniting and dividing again, demonstrating the content of the Chorus' speeches.

Chorus
> Two sisters quarrel
> The weight of centuries
> On young shoulders
> The bond breaks
> And the crack spreads
> Dividing brother against sister
> Father against son
> Mother against daughter
> Bitterness erupts
> Fear spreads like a virus
> Peace is tossed like a fox
> Among bloodhounds
> Spades that planted roots
> Now bury the dead
> The sweet pain of desire
> Once played as a game for innocents
> Is now released like a wild beast

And all that's seen is taken
The screams of the dying are now as common
As the final lowing of a slaughtered calf
Or the last bleats and squeals
Of lamb or pig
The world becomes a slaughterhouse
Mothers, daughters, sons and fathers
Grandmothers, sisters, uncles, brothers
Families cleaved into single souls
Single souls carved into
A hundred warring fears

*The Chorus builds to a huge crescendo: a scream
synchronised with a thunderous crash, then everything
goes quiet.*

So turns the world
So turn the mills of hate

*A hillside.
    Chaff, Butt and Lena sit around the remains of a
fire.*

Chaff I'm starving.
Lena We're all starving. The whole country's starving,
thanks to you.
Butt Lena, it wasn't her fault.
Lena No, I know, but you have to have someone to
blame.
Butt Why?
Lena It makes you feel better, that's why! Sometimes,
Butt, I wonder if you know anything that isn't written
in a book.
Butt Don't you start.

*Josef enters. His head is covered. He is carrying a long
knife and a sack of turnips.*

Lena Who are you?

Butt We don't want any trouble. We wanted no part of this war.

Lena He's got a knife. He's going to kill us!

Josef That's right. I have a sharp knife and in this sack I have the heads of sheep-herders that I have slaughtered.

Lena Oh my God!

Josef empties the sack on the floor. The turnips roll out.

Turnips!

Josef Yes. Help yourself. (*He uncovers his head.*)

Chaff It's you, the goatboy who came back from the dead! What are you doing here?

Lena Why have you come here? To kill us?

Josef Yesterday I would have. Yesterday I was a hero, a saint.

Butt What happened?

Josef Word travelled. They found out I'd been brought back to life by the devil. Now I am a traitor, an outcast.

Chaff You're welcome to stay with us.

Josef Thanks. Help yourself to the turnips.

They eat the raw turnips.

Butt Have you heard how the war is going?

Josef Last time I heard we were winning.

Butt No, you must be mistaken. We were winning.

Chaff We?

Butt That is to say, our people, well OK, the sheep-people were winning.

Josef The last figures were twenty thousand sheep culled to your nineteen thousand six hundred goats.

Lena A clear-cut victory to the goat-people obviously.

Long pause.

Chaff You know what I think.

Lena What?

Chaff I think we should go and see the Virgin.

They stare at her perplexed.
Crossfade to another part of the mountains.
Mermer, Clove, Gregor, Grimm, Mendel and Brag
are huddled together. They are arguing.

Mermer . . . I won't do it! I won't eat goat!

Clove We have no choice, Mermer. Brag found a kid
dead at the bottom of a gully. It's fresh. We are
starving.

Grimm Goat meat shall not soil these lips.

Gregor Granpa is right.

Clove No, he isn't right, Gregor! We have no food. That
kid is food!

Gregor Never!

Brag Don't be so stubborn, Gregor. We must eat.

Gregor You've changed your tune.

Brag I'm hungry.

Gregor Where are your principles?

Brag Where are your brains?

Gregor This is our way of life. This is what we are
fighting for. Not to be contaminated by the unclean!

Mendel Mother, I want to see Chaff again.

Mermer Don't mention that one's name here!

Clove No, Mermer, we will mention her. I want to see
my daughter again too. I'm sick of this war.

Gregor But we're winning.

Clove If this is winning, I can't imagine what it's like to
lose. Mermer, I want you to get off my back.

Mermer What?

Clove You heard. Get down off my back. I've had
enough. And if Gregor had any sense, he'd put you
down too, Granpa. Both of you can walk for God's
sake!

Grimm That's not the point. We've earned the right to
sit on your backs.

Mermer This is how I carried you when you were a
child. Besides it's tradition.

Clove Well, it's about time things changed. Get down.
Now. Go on.

Mermer I won't.

Clove Yes you will. Or I'll just let you fall.

Mermer You wouldn't dare!

Clove Try me.

Mermer (*reluctantly getting down*) You'll regret this.
This is against all our customs. Oh, I can't stand . . .
I'm going to . . . fall!

They watch her fall and flail on the ground.

I can't walk! Clove, I've forgotten how to walk!

Clove You'll learn again. Now, Granpa, down you
come. Gregor.

Gregor What will the priest say?

Clove I don't care what the priest says. We're not
carrying these two if they're perfectly capable of
walking. Granpa, down!

Grimm You wouldn't let her do this, son, would you?

Gregor I'm too weak to support you any more, father.

*Gregor releases Grimm's feet from the stirrups and he
goes crashing to the ground. He flails about with
Mermer.*

Grimm Aaaaaah! Help me, someone, I can't walk! We
are being cruelly treated by our own children! There is
no respect any more!

Gregor Clove, have we done the right thing?

Clove I don't know, but I certainly feel a lot better. Let's
go.

Mendel Where are we going?

Clove To see the Virgin. Come on, Gregor, Mendel.
Brag, bring the kid. Mermer and Grimm, follow on
when you've got the hang of walking again.

Clove strides off with Mendel, Gregor following. Brag stares open-mouthed, while Mermer and Grimm flail about on the floor, trying to remember how to walk.

The Mount of the Virgin of the Sheep People.

Chorus
So they came in pilgrimage
To the Mount of the Virgin
A mother to see her daughter
Sister to be reunited with sister
A whisper stirs into
The thunder of peace

Two groups move towards the mountain: Butt, Lena, Josef, Chaff and Clove, Mendel, Gregor, Grimm, Mermer, Brag.

They reach a mid-point and stand looking at each other.

They cannot speak
Their mouths are stopped up
With old hate
Cold hurt
Dried insults
Spattered pride
They simply stand and stare
Unsure of why they are here
Or what they are supposed to do
How much do you want peace?
What would you sacrifice
To cradle the trembling dove
In your hands?

Both sides of the family extend their hands to each other, tentatively, then drop them. They hang their heads and turn away.

Peace is a foreign country
When war has been your home
For far too long

Mendel Mother, speak to them.

Clove I can't! They seem so strange to me now.

Mendel Granpa, you say something.

Grimm Words come into my throat, child, and then they choke me.

Mendel Mermer?

Mermer No.

Mendel Brag, what about you?

There is a long pause. Brag is fighting something within himself. Then:

Brag You turned against us!

Clove Brag, no!

Brag Yes. You took sides against your own. You broke up the family. You deserve to be punished!

Chaff You are the ones who deserve to be punished! You and your pig-headedness!

Chorus
So begin all peace talks
With a lot of shouting

Mendel Chaff, don't, please! We are supposed to be making peace.

Mermer We can't make peace. We are too old for that.

Grimm How can we talk to you when you have that goatherd with you!

Chaff Because you must. See, he's not a monster. He's the same as we are.

Josef I wouldn't say that.

Chaff What!

Josef Well, goatherds were here first. In the mountains. It's well-known. The sheep came much later.

Gregor You see! That's the kind of people we're dealing with. Arrogant. Wrong-headed. Dangerous.

Brag (*drawing his knife*) You won't survive a second
time, goatherd!

Josef That remains to be seen!

*Josef draws his knife and he and Brag circle each
other.*

Chorus
So begin all peace-talks
With violence

Clove We've come to talk peace, not to start fighting all
over again. Put those knives away! Both of you!

Brag No.

Josef No.

Lena Why not?

Brag The sheep-people cannot make concessions in an
ongoing conflict situation. It is unreasonable to make
these demands in an atmosphere of heightened tension
and the goat-people must acknowledge the status quo.

Gregor What's he talking about?

Josef Whilst not wishing to jeopardise the peace talks
in any way, the goat-people are not convinced that it
would be in their best interests to abrogate the use of
armed force.

Lena What?

Sylvian So begin all peace-talks. With a lot of bullshit.

Gregor They're not ready for peace.

Clove Neither are we. We have to make ourselves ready.

Gregor Why here? Why now?

Clove Why not?

Butt This is the usual pattern, you see. Studies prove it.
It's a cycle.

Lena But the cycle can be broken.

Gregor How?

Lena It must be, or we'll be condemned to go on living
like this for ever.

Clove Everyone seems to have forgotten this is a shrine. We are here to petition the Virgin for help.

The Virgin appears from the Chorus.

Virgin I wondered when I was going to get a look in.
Mermer Who are you?
Virgin The Virgin of the Mountains, if that's all right with you.
Mermer But you look so . . . ordinary.
Virgin What you see is what you get. I am what you made me. I thought you might want to meet my opposite number from the south.

A Second Virgin appears from the Chorus.

Chaff Who's that?
Josef That is our Virgin!
Second Virgin That's right. Hello, Josef. Bad news about your miracle, but that was strictly speaking out of my jurisdiction.
Mermer There can't be two Virgins!
Second Virgin Why not?
Mermer Because . . . because it's like saying there are two moons. Ours is the only Virgin.
Second Virgin Nope, sorry granma, but the goat-people have got one as well.
Josef There is only one Virgin and that is our Virgin. The other is an imposter!
Virgin Did you hear what he called me?
Second Virgin He must be a priest.
Virgin Look, Josef whatever your name is, pin your ears back and listen to me for a minute. Heaven is just full of angels and gods and prophets and saints and martyrs and holy animals and God knows what and there's more of them coming in every day. You wouldn't believe the things people pray to.

Second Virgin So don't come round here telling us who's genuine and who isn't because not even we know that, all right? You can fight about that amongst yourselves.

Virgin And they do.

Clove Can you help us find peace?

Virgin If you mean can I or my friend here find it for you, the answer is no.

Mermer So what do we light candles and say prayers to you for then?

Virgin Search me. You started all that business.

Clove Please. Tell us what we can do.

Second Virgin I think you'll find peace is about sacrifice, but that's all I can really say at the moment.

Grimm Sacrifice? You mean like offering the blood of a slaughtered lamb?

Second Virgin Come on grandad, don't you think we've had enough of that to last us a lifetime?

Virgin Good luck anyway. We'll be rooting for you.

The Virgins merge back into the Chorus.

Mermer Fat lot of use they were.

Clove No, she had a point. What would you give up for peace Mermer?

Mermer Haven't I made enough sacrifices?

Josef Well, I could do without this. There's too much blood on it.

Josef throws his knife into the ring of stones that serves as a hearth.

Chorus
  A naked eye stares down steel
  The dove challenges the hawk
  To do something outside its nature
  But the hawk cannot fly with the dove
  And the dove cannot fly with the hawk

All images falter
Bitter memories bear sweet fruit
Only when the thoughts of human minds
Transform them
And the hawk coos
The dove hovers
The gun barrel spouts pure water
Raking thirsty hearts with bullets of rain.

Clove What about you, Brag?

Brag How will I defend myself?

Chaff There can't be any peace until you throw it down.

Brag How do I know I can trust him?

Butt You don't. That's trust.

Brag I can't. There's too much history.

Chaff History is something you learn from, Brag. You look at the past and you change. You don't just carry on as before.

Brag They hate us. We hate them. It's how things are. How they've always been.

Clove Throw down your knife, Brag. Take a risk. You have the courage for that.

Brag I don't know . . .

Chaff Throw it down, Brag.

After a long struggle, Brag throws his knife in too. They cheer.

Chaff I just want to be with my sister again.

Mendel So do I. Will you join the cord again, Chaff?

Chaff No.

Mendel No?

Chaff No. We can still be together without being tied to each other.

Mendel How?

Chaff Like this. Together when we want to be. Apart when we want to be.

Mendel and Chaff hold hands.

Mendel What about Granpa and Mermer? They still can't walk.
Mermer Heartless children!
Clove We can't carry them any more. They can learn again how to stand.
Gregor And if they don't?
Clove It's downhill all the way home. We can roll them.
Mermer Did I give birth to such a monster! I won't walk! I'm staying here to die!
Chaff That's your choice, Mermer.

Grimm and Mermer beat their fists on the ground in frustration and try to stand, but find it very difficult.

Chorus
Things that have been flung apart
Now join again
Peace enters the heart like a dream
Filling every corner with its light
Who can say how long this peace will last
Who can say if its hard lesson
Will need to be learned again and again
Down the generations
One thing is certain:
The dream of peace
Must be held like a butterfly
In hands at once delicate and strong
All Peace!

Music and dance.
    Suddenly, Sylvian the treeman comes into view, hanging from his branch.

Sylvian Do you want the good news first or the bad news?

The good news is the war is over.
You can all go home.
The bad news is: cattle-herders are bringing cows
through the northern pass.

Final music and end of play.

Online Resources for Secondary Schools and Colleges

To support the use of *Connections* plays in the Drama studio and the English classroom, extensive resources are available exclusively online. The material aims not only to make the most of new technologies, but also to be accessible and easy to use

Visit *www.connectionsplays.co.uk* for activities exploring each of the plays in a wide range of categories

- Speaking and Listening
- Writing
- Reading and Response
- Practical Drama
- Plays in Production
- Themes

Carefully tailored tasks – whether for KS3, KS4 or A-Level – are accompanied by clear learning objectives; National Curriculum links; ideas for extension and development, and for differentiation; Internet links; and assessment opportunities

The material has been compiled by a team of practising English and Drama teachers, headed by Andy Kempe, author of *The GCSE Drama Coursebook* and (with Lionel Warner) *Starting with Scripts: Dramatic Literature for Key Stages 3 & 4*

STANLEY THORNES